P9-CFQ-167

THE STORY OF
GRETTIR THE STRONG

"Fool, Awake!" Said Angle Again

THE STORY OF
Grettir the Strong

By
ALLEN FRENCH

GRETTIR THE STRONG

E. P. DUTTON & CO., INC.
NEW YORK

TABLE OF CONTENTS

TABLE OF CONTENTS

PREFACE

AMONG Icelandic sagas there are two which, from their human interest and literary perfection, deserve to be classed with world-literature. The first of these is the Njal's Saga, the second the Grettir's Saga; both of them have been in English form for about forty years, but because the translations faithfully followed the originals they never became popular, especially since this branch of literature, of great importance in illustrating the development of the northern races, has in our schools been neglected in favor of the poetry and mythology of the Greeks and Romans.

Valuable as are the classic tales, there is to be drawn from them no such lesson of manliness as the northern stories teach. If I wished a lad to learn from his reading the quality of steadfast courage, I would put into his hands these two Icelandic sagas, with the Morte d'Arthur and even the Niebelungen Lied, rather than the Iliad, the Odyssey, or the Æneid. There is only one book whose tales surpass these northern stories in teaching the lesson of manly self-dependence, and that book is the Bible.

Widely known as are the Njal's and the Grettir's Sagas, they have come, as I said, very little into popularity on account of their original mass of detail, which although invaluable for the student confuses the general reader. Following my "Heroes of Iceland," which a year ago I adapted from Dasent's translation of "Burnt Njal," I have now worked into more available shape the translation of the Grettir's Saga, which was published in 1869 by William Morris and Eirikr Magnusson.

The work of these two adaptations differed widely. The original of the Njal's Saga is so clear and straight-forward, and the translation so simple and fine, that the adaptation was little more than an abridgment. But the Grettir's Saga is cumbered with incidents of little value, from which the true thread of the story must be disentangled. Besides this, Morris's phrasing is so poetical and involved that in many places the meaning is obscure.

I have therefore felt obliged to re-
write the story from end to end, for
younger readers, making such changes
in the action or chronology of the story
as would produce a connected whole,
and rejecting all unnecessary or un-
interesting parts. Short as it is, my
version presents the essentials of the
Grettir's Saga, and gives, besides the
story of the hero, a view of the life
and superstitions of the Iceland of his
day. One liberty I have taken with
the story which I trust will be justified.
The medieval writer of the saga bor-
rowed, for the end of the book, an un-
pleasant incident from Gottfried von
Strasburg's "Tristan und Isolde." I
have taken the liberty of using in the
final chapter another incident of the
Tristan story as found in the same
poem.

As for the original of the story, it was probably first written during the thirteenth century, Grettir himself having been born about the year 997, or three years before the conversion of Iceland to Christianity. In spite of the many supernatural incidents found in the story, Grettir was doubtless a real man, and the saga shows him as he must have been, no merry outlaw such as Robin Hood, but a grand and tragic character.

For a discussion of Iceland in its heroic age I must refer my readers to the preface and introduction to my "Heroes of Iceland." The Grettir's Saga shows the Icelanders to be much as in the Njal's Saga, but in addition gives glimpses of their superstitions, in the tales of trolls and sprites, giants and witches, all whom are pictured as disappearing before the power of Christianity.

ALLEN FRENCH.

CONCORD, MASSACHUSETTS
March, 1906.

ILLUSTRATIONS

THE STORY OF GRETTIR THE STRONG

CHAPTER I

OF GRETTIR AND KARR THE OLD

GRETTIR the Strong, Grettir the Outlaw, one of the heroes of his race, was born, men say, in the year 997, at Biarg in Iceland. A man of great heart and high spirit was he, yet unlucky, doomed to a sad end. His foes were many and his misfortunes great, but he lived like a man, and like a man he died.

Asmund was his father, Asdis his mother; his sisters are not of account, but his elder brother was Atli, whose death he avenged; his younger brother

1

was Illugi, who died with him; and his half-brother was Thorstein Dromund, who avenged him.

Of Grettir's youth there are few tales told, and he was not thought to be a lad of promise. He was of large growth and for a long time unwieldy; his speech was rough and jesting, and he gave way to none. He yielded obedience scarcely even to his father, and made scoffing rhymes upon any who displeased him. He was still but a lad when he slew a man who would have slain him. So hot were the man's kinsmen over the blood-suit that though all fines were paid Grettir was outlawed from Iceland for three winters.

His father gave him little for his outfit, and refused him weapons, lest with them he should make more trouble. But his mother went with him a little way upon the road, and at parting said to him: "Thou mayest come into great danger, and a weapon may save thy life." Then she drew out from under her cloak her grandfather's sword, a famous weapon, and gave it to him, and sent him on his way with her blessing.

He took ship and paid his passage, and when they cleared the land he made himself a sleeping-place under the ship's boat that was stowed upon the deck, and there he spent his time, sleeping and getting his meals, and refusing to help in the work of the ship. The weather grew rough and the ship was leaky, so that men had to take turns in bailing her out (for in those days there were no ship's pumps), but Grettir would not stir to help, and instead scoffed at the men so that they threatened to take his life when once they were ashore. The leak gained on the men after many days of labor; then the captain went to Grettir and bade him work if he would not drown. Grettir went to the bailers and offered his help.

They were so angry with him that they would not take his aid until the captain begged them. Then they set him in the ship's well, and two men were to take the bailers from him, but he soon tired them out. Then four men were set to help him, but they could not work fast enough for him. So at last eight men bailed against him, and they had their hands full until the work was done. Then they all praised him for his strength and his endurance, and from that time he was

ready with his help. But the end of
the voyage was that they were wrecked
near the island of Haramsey, which is
off the coast of Norway.

Thorfinn, the son of Karr the Old,
was then the lord of Haramsey and a
powerful chief in the realm of Norway.
He sent his boat to the wreck and
saved all the lives and much of the
goods. The rest of the ship's people
soon went to the mainland, but Grettir
remained there upon Haramsey in the
house of Thorfinn.

Thorfinn was bountiful and hos-
pitable; all men were welcome who
came to his house, but he wished those
who ate his food to give him their
company when he went about, and to
be merry in his presence. But Grettir
was glum and of few words, and as for
following Thorfinn, he went about en-

tirely by himself. Thorfinn was not pleased with him, yet would not send him from his house.

Grettir went freely among the farms, entered the houses, and talked with the men; with one of them named Audun he became friends. Grettir went oftenest to Audun's farm, and frequently sat there with him into the evening. Now one night when it was late Grettir saw a great fire burst out upon a point of land where there was no house nor barn nor anything that might take fire, but only a great burial mound.

"What can that fire be?" asked Grettir. But Audun would not say.

"In Iceland," said Grettir, "that would be called a sign of hidden treasure."

"That may be true in Norway also,"

answered Audun, "but the treasure that lies hid beneath that fire is not for thee and me to meddle with, but only for the bishop or very holy men."

"Is there then so strong a spirit that guards the treasure?" asked Grettir. "And who lies buried in the mound?"

Audun said: "That is the barrow of Karr the Old, Thorfinn's father. And by means of Karr has Thorfinn come into all his wealth." Then he told how at first Thorfinn had owned but one farm in the island; but Karr had so haunted the other farms that their owners had either fled and sold them to Thorfinn, or else had sold to him and remained as his tenants. For Karr haunted none of his son's men, and now that Thorfinn owned all the island Karr was seen no more, but the flame still burned often above his barrow.

"Good," said Grettir. "Now I must see what treasures are hidden there, and when I come to-morrow do thou have ready a rope, a pickaxe, and a spade." And though Audun begged him to do nothing, for fear of Thorfinn's anger, or of Karr himself, Grettir said he would take all risks. He came again on the morrow, and both of them went to the barrow, with rope and tools.

The barrow was huge; rafters like those of a house had been laid together for its frame, and over them was heaped much earth. Grettir dug till he came to the rafters, and then with much labor he broke through those; by the time he had made a hole large enough for his body, it was evening, and

Audun begged him to come away, for at night the ghost could walk. But Grettir said he would not leave the work unfinished. He drove a stake, and tied the rope to it, and told Audun to be ready to pull him up. He had no torch, but slid down the rope into the darkness of the barrow.

Then Grettir groped about in that place. He found the skull of a horse, for before men became Christian it was the custom to sacrifice horses at burials, and those heathen times had but lately passed away. Then he found coins and jewels lying in a heap: there were great rings and brooches, with chains, cups, and drinking-horns of strange shapes. And then he tripped in the darkness, and fell forward, and plunged into the lap of Karr himself, who sat there dead. Grettir caught

him by the arms, but he did not stir;
he had been a strong man, very large
of frame. Grettir felt and found that
he was in armor, and a short sword
hung at one side of his chair, with a
great barbed spear leaning at the other.
Nothing further was to be found in
the barrow except a chest of money,
placed under the dead man's feet.

Grettir took the treasures to the
rope, but when he tried to take the
arms he could not move them. Then
he lashed the booty to the rope, and
was calling to Audun to pull it up,
when the spirit seized him from behind.

Before the grip was fast, Grettir
broke loose and turned about, and
gripped him in return. But the onset
of the ghost was so fierce that Grettir
gave way before it, and strove to fight
him off. But that would not do, and

Grettir saw that he must do his best or else lose his life there quickly. Then with all his force he thrust aside Karr's arms and caught him by the waist, and in the darkness they wrestled there for a long time, and lurched against the seat and broke it, and fought among the horse bones. At last by a mighty effort Grettir lifted the ghost and cast him down upon his back, and fell upon him with great noise. Audun from the barrow-top called Grettir's name, but he had no breath to answer, and Audun fled away in fear of his own life.

Then Grettir drew his sword and cut off the head of Karr, and laid it at his thigh, for by no other method can a ghost be laid. But when he called to Audun, no answer came, and Grettir had to climb the rope.

He pulled up the treasure after him, and was starting homeward, when he thought that perchance he might now be able to take those weapons from the chair, since the ghost was laid. Down he went again into the barrow, found the sword and the spear, took them, and climbed out again with them.

Grettir walked, very stiff and lame, to Thorfinn's house, loaded with the treasures and the weapons. He came in late, when the meal was all but finished.

Said Thorfinn sourly: "Canst thou not come to meals on time?"

Grettir answered: "A little matter kept me." And with that he cast upon the table before Thorfinn his load of arms and treasure. Last of all he laid down the short-sword, which he had been carrying in his hand, and

Grettir Walked very Stiff and Lame

the feel of which he liked so well that he was unwilling to part from it. In the light he saw that it was a beautiful weapon, and he laid it down grudgingly, while all those in the hall crowded to see what he had brought. Thorfinn looked at all the treasure and the weapons, and was silent for a while; but then he asked where Grettir got all those. Grettir sang:

"In the barrow by the sea,
There this treasure came to me.
He that seeketh there for more
Surely will find little store."

Thorfinn said: "Did the dweller in the barrow give these up without a struggle?"

Grettir sang agan:

"Neither arms nor gold gave he
To my wardship willingly.
And now nevermore again

Will he be seen on hill or plain.
— For this service is the sword
From thee to me too great reward?"

Thorfinn shook his head. "Because nowadays we think," said he, "that treasure should not be hidden away, I cannot blame thee for breaking into the barrow. But as to the sword, thou must prove thyself worthy of it before I give it to thee, for it has always been a great heirloom in my house."

Grettir shrugged his shoulders and asked no more. Thorfinn took the treasure to himself, and hung the spear and the short-sword by his bed.

CHAPTER II

GRETTIR AND THE BARESARKS

GRETTIR lived in Thorfinn's house into the winter, but he was no more friendly than before, and the household cared little for him. When it was Christmas-time, Thorfinn made ready to go to his Yule-feast. The feast was to be on the mainland, where he had a farm; all his tenants and many of his friends were to come, but just before the feast Thorfinn's little daughter fell sick so that she could not go, and her mother had to stay with her to care for her. Thorfinn was at first unwilling to leave them, but at last he went away, thinking them safe

with Grettir and eight men, for no outlaws were lately in the neighborhood.

But in other years there had been
bands of outlaws and baresarks that
preyed on the land, living on the
barren islands and coming and going
in their ships. These men did such
great harm that Thorfinn had pleaded
with the Earl to send men against
them and drive them from the land.
This the Earl did, and many of the
outlaws were slain, and many fled
away. Now two brothers were the
worst of all the baresarks, Thorir
Paunch and Ogmund the Evil, great
robbers and very violent men; but it
was thought they and their crew had
also fled, and thus it was that Thorfinn
went away to the mainland for the
feast, leaving so few men on the island
to guard the buildings and the women.

When it came to the day before Christmas Thorfinn's daughter was so well that she could walk outdoors. From the island all day ships could be seen coming and going along the coast, bearing neighbors to each other's feasts. The sun went down and the women went indoors, but Grettir stayed and watched the ships. Then he saw one ship that made for the island; it was small and weather-beaten, but it was a ship of warriors, for shields hung along its bulwarks. Though few men rowed, it came swiftly, and made for Thorfinn's landing-place, below his boat-sheds. The oarsmen drove the ship smartly upon the beach, and springing out they ran it higher up. Grettir counted twelve men in all, and liked them little.

In the boat-shed was Thorfinn's

largest boat, to launch which needed thirty men. But these twelve easily ran it out upon the shore, and taking up their own craft they put it in the shed. The men then took their weapons from the ship and girded themselves; they were all well armed. Then they saw Grettir where he stood watching them, and pointed him out to each other.

So Grettir, seeing that there was nothing better to do, went down to them on the beach, and welcomed them, and asked who they were.

There were two that appeared to be leaders, and one of them spoke and said that he was called Thorir Paunch, and his brother was Ogmund.

"Is Thorfinn at home?" asked he.

"I know of you," said Grettir, "and this is an hour of good fortune for you, as it will be bad for Thorfinn. He is away, and has left only me behind, and some thralls, and his wife and child. And now everything lies before you to do with as you please. As for my own grudge against him, it can now be well paid."

Then Thorir said to his brother: "It has all happened as I hoped. Now we can revenge ourselves on Thorfinn for making us outlaws."

"Now," said Grettir, "come home with me to Thorfinn's house, for I see you are wet with the waves, and you shall have whatever you need."

So they followed him to the hall, and he welcomed them when they came to the door, and made them welcome with many words. There was the mistress decking the house for the morrow, and she stood still when she

heard Grettir speaking so much, who
was usually so silent; she asked what
guests had come. He told her that
there were Thorir Paunch and Ogmund
the Evil, who had come to spend Yule.

"Now," she cried, "I would have
given anything if this had not happened. A wicked man art thou, to betray our goods into their hands and
our buildings to their torches. We
took thee from the shipwreck and have
fed and housed thee ever since, and
now we shall be turned out into the
snow."

"It would be wiser for thee," answered Grettir, "to serve thy guests."

But she, and her little daughter, and
all the women, rushed away weeping,
and the house-carles slunk away one
by one out of the hall. "See," said
Grettier, "we came upon them hastily

and frightened them. Give me your wet clothes and your weapons, and dry yourselves at the fire. I will hang up your things to dry, and will fetch food and drink."

They gave him their weapons and their outer clothes, and he laid them away; then he brought them meat and drink. He sat and talked with them, and told them tales, and made them merry, so that Thorir and Ogmund were pleased with him, and asked what reward they should give him for his help.

"When the booty is all heaped together," answered Grettir, "then perhaps you will let me choose one or two little things."

"Good," said Thorir. "That pleases us well, and now we will swear fellowship with vows."

"Not so," replied Grettir. "I think little of vows made so hastily. Wait until the morning, or until ye have known me four-and-twenty hours, and then see if we are of the same mind."

They agreed to that. Then when they had finished eating, Grettir said: "Come with me to Thorfinn's treasure-house, and let me show you what goods ye have won here so bloodlessly."

So they were glad, and went with him to Thorfinn's storehouse, a very strong place, with steps leading up to it, and passages inside, and locked rooms. Grettir led them in, and showed them Thorfinn's stores, and these pleased the baresarks much. So he led them further in, to one of the locked rooms, and there were kept all of Thorfinn's best cloths, and his hangings, which were very handsome.

Thorir and Ogmund stood and admired, but the others began horse-play with each other and with Grettir. Then in the confusion he slipped away from them, and out of the room, and locked the door behind him, and they did not miss him. But he rushed back to the house with all speed.

The women had hidden, and the men were cowering in fear, and they had not dared even to bar the door against the baresarks. Grettir rushed in and called the mistress; she was hidden and dared not answer.

"Now," called Grettir to her again, "give me the best weapons that thou hast, for it is thy last chance."

So she came out of her hiding, and led him to Thorfinn's locked bed, and showed him where hung a helm, with

the spear and the sword which Grettir
had taken from the barrow. He put
on the helm and snatched the weapons,
and rushed out again. Then the mistress went to the house-carles and bade
them arm and follow Grettir; but only
four of them dared take their weapons,
while the other four hung back and
would not come out of hiding.

Meanwhile the baresarks grew tired
of looking at Thorfinn's belongings,
and missed Grettir from among them.
First they waited for him to come back,
but then they tried the door and found
it locked, and saw that here was trick-
ery. They threw themselves against
the door and the walls so that the whole
building rocked and creaked. Fury
overcame them; they foamed at the
mouth and howled like wolves; then
their strength grew with their madness,

till they broke out into the passageway and came out to the steps. Then
as they came to the top of the steps
and howled there in their fury, Grettir
came running up, holding the spear
with both hands.

He thrust at once with the spear at
Thorir, who was coming down the
steps; Ogmund, who came after, ran
upon his brother and pushed him forward. The spear went through Thorir
and stood a foot out from his back,
and Ogmund himself tumbled upon
the point and was slain. Both rolled
down the steps dead together; Grettir
drew the spear away, and held it in
his left hand while the sword was in
his right, and turned upon the other
ten as they came howling down the
steps.

But he had to give back before the

weight of their onslaught, and so they fought upon the home-mead in the dusk. Grettir thrust with the spear or struck with the sword; but the baresarks took up logs that lay there, and smote with them, or hurled them at him, so that the danger was great. The house-carles came up to join in the fight, but they dared not strike in boldly, and came close only when the baresarks turned away, giving ground when the outlaws turned upon them. Two vikings Grettir slew before the house-carles came, and two after that; then the baresarks fled to their boat, and took refuge in the boat-shed. There they seized the oars to use as weapons.

The house-carles did not dare to enter that dark place, where the outlaws were; but Grettir went in boldly, and the house-carles, fearing that he would drive the others out, slipped away to the homestead, where they boasted of their bravery. The mistress tried to drive them forth again to help Grettir, but it was now nearly dark and snow was falling, and they would not go.

But Grettir, entering into the boat-shed in the darkness, with no shield to guard him, was set upon by the vikings and battered by the oars. Yet he rushed among them and got within their guard; then he struck with the short-sword and heard the groans of stricken men. One fell dead at his feet; he stepped over the fallen body, and while the vikings gave way he pressed after and struck hard. Then another fell, but the other four dodged around the boat and so got out into the open.

Grettir ran out after them and saw

where two fled in one direction and
two in another; he followed those two
that went by the way nearest the
homestead, and nearly lost them in the
darkness and the snow. They fled
to Audun's farm, but Audun was away
with Thorfinn to the mainland, and
Grettir saw no one whom he could
call to help. The baresarks fled into
an out-house and would have shut the
door, but Grettir burst in upon them
and set upon them there in the dark.
This time he guarded the door, so
that they should not again get by him,
and there he slew first one and then
the other.

By now the night was pitch black,
and where the other two vikings had
gone he could not guess. He was so
weary with his work and his bruises
that he would have lain down there to

sleep; but he remembered the danger of those at Thorfinn's house, and set out thither to guard the women. And there in the darkness and the snow he might have lost himself and died of cold, but the mistress at Thorfinn's house set lights in the upper windows to guide him on his way. So at last he came to the house and stumbled in at the door nearly spent.

The mistress ran up to him and welcomed him, giving him great praise. Said Grettir: "I am no different than I was but a few hours ago, when you all so hated me."

"I knew not," answered she, "the scheme that was in thy mind, nor the great heart that thou hadst to carry it out. But now every honor that I can do thee I will, and when Thorfinn returns he will reward thee well."

"Well," said Grettir, "we will speak of reward when it is time, for there are two of the vikings left."

Then he took a little food and drink, and watched in the hall until morning. At daybreak the house-carles were sent out to gather help, and when the men had come together Grettir led them to search for the two baresarks. For a long time they could not be found, but at last they were seen by boys, lying together in the shelter of a rock, where there was no snow. But when Grettir went in on them the baresarks were dead; they had bled to death from their wounds, and now were frozen stiff. So then all twelve of the baresarks were brought to one place on the shore, and were buried in the shingle.

Grettir went home and told the mistress how all twelve of those vikings had got their deaths at his hand. She said that there were few living men that were his equal, and he not yet a man, nor come to his full strength. Then she set him in the high-seat, and did him every honor until the time of Thorfinn's return. When he was told that Thorfinn's ship was seen coming Grettir bade no one go to meet him, but all to stay in the house; "for," said he, "it will do him no harm to be frightened at what he may see, and to remember that he left small guard here at home."

Now Thorfinn in his ship came near the landing, and saw there his own great boat lying on the shore, and began to question who had been there. "Pull quickly, men," said he, "for surely something has gone wrong here at home." So they pulled hard at the oars, and when they drove the ship ashore Thorfinn was the first to leap from her. He went up to the boat-shed, and there he found the ship of the baresarks, and knew it at once.

Said he to his men: "Now I fear that a great evil has come upon me, to avoid which I would have given everything I own."

They asked him what he meant.

"This," said he, "is the ship of those baresarks Thorir Paunch and Ogmund the Evil, and I greatly dread what they may have done here in my absence. For the thralls would do little against them, and little is to be looked for from the surly Icelander." Then he led his men homeward in haste.

But the goodwife, when she saw

that her husband's ship had come to
shore, begged that she and her daughter
might go to meet him. Grettir gave
them leave, but himself stayed behind and toasted his shins by the fire.
She and the little girl ran to meet
Thorfinn, and when he saw them
coming joyfully his heart was lightened,
and he praised God. When he had
kissed them he asked the meaning of
what he had found.

Said his wife: "Great loss would
have come upon us but for Grettir."
And while he listened she told him
what had happened. Then she led
Thorfinn to the hall, and there was
Grettir sitting.

Thorfinn went straight to him, and
clapped his hands upon his shoulders,
and kissed him. And Thorfinn said:
"I owe thee more than I can ever re-

pay save by saving thy own life. And
this I wish, that some day I may find
thee in need, so that I can help thee as
thou hast helped me."   And he begged
Grettir to stay there as long as he
wished, and to take the place of honor
at his right hand.

So Grettir stayed there the winter
through, and not until the spring did
he go out again upon his journeys.
When he made ready to go Thorfinn
offered him money, but Grettir would
let him pay only his passage to the
mainland. Then Thorfinn put him
on board the ship, and at parting he
gave Grettir the short-sword, Karr's
loom, and begged him to call on him
whenever he was in need.

CHAPTER III

GRETTIR AND THE BEAR, AND THE BROTHERS OF BIORN

GRETTIR spent that summer in Norway, in many places, and wherever he came he was welcomed because of his deed in slaying the baresarks. By autumn he came to Helgoland, and there he was invited to spend the winter with a man named Thorkel, a chief of good family. So Grettir stayed there in Thorkel's house.

Now Thorkel had a kinsman named Biorn who dwelt with him, a trouble-maker and a tale-bearer. He wished to lord it over Grettir, but Grettir was stiff against him, yet also silent, so that Biorn had to satisfy himself with biting words. But other young fellows followed Biorn, and lived riotously, drinking much and going about at night with loud singing and great noise. Before Christmas a bear was roused from his winter sleep, and went nightly abroad ravaging; men said it was Biorn and his crew that had roused him. The bear was so bold and strong that he broke into barns and sheepfolds, and did much damage among the herds and flocks. Dogs were afraid of him, and the farmers dared not go near him.

Thorkel was the richest man in the district, and his flocks suffered the most. So at last he gathered his men and searched for the den of the beast, till they found it in the cliff by the sea, with but a narrow path leading to it, and sheer rocks below, down which it would be death to fall.

"Now," said Biorn, "the worst is done, since we have found the lair. Now let us go home, and it will later be seen what we two namesakes will make out of this." This he said boasting, for his own name, Biorn, was Icelandic for bear.

So they went home, and that evening about bedtime Biorn slipped away from the others, and went to the path to the den, and lay down with this shield over him, meaning to stab the bear with his sword when he passed over him. Certain of Biorn's companions had watched him, and saw where he went, and spied from a distance to see what would happen. But the bear was so slow in coming out that Biorn fell asleep. Then out came

the bear, and sniffed at the man, and
pawed him over. He clawed the shield
away and hurled it over the cliff just
as Biorn woke. Then Biorn leaped
up and ran away, and barely saved
his life. His friends saw that, and
in the morning they led others to see
his shield, and laughed at Biorn
continually.

Before long Thorkel lost more of his
cattle by the brute, so at last he took
eight men, and went to the lair of the
bear, and tried to kill him. Biorn
was there, and so was Grettir; now
Grettir had on a fine fur cloak, which
he laid aside for the fight. Biorn
egged on the others, but was not very
forward himself; and as for Grettir,
he found the number of them on the
narrow path gave no good room for
fighting, so he could do little. The

bear kept inside his cave, and all they could do was to thrust at him with spears, which he turned aside. So they accomplished nothing except the breaking of good weapons. But while they were still trying to get at the bear Biorn seized Grettir's cloak and cast it into the lair. The bear gathered it under him out of the way, and at first Grettir did not see what had been done.

But when at last after all their work they saw they could not slay the bear, and turned away toward home, then Grettir missed his cloak, and saw that it was in the den. Said he: "Who has thrown my cloak in there?"

Biorn answered, "He who will own to it."

"Well," said Grettir, "it is of no account."

So they went home, and before they

had gone far Grettir's shoe-thong broke, and he sat down to mend it, and told the others not to wait for him.

"Ah," said Biorn, jeering, "I see that he means to stay behind and get his cloak."

Thorkel told him not to scoff, lest the reply be too sharp for him, but Biorn said that he would choose his own words. So they went on and left Grettir behind.

But when they were out of sight over the hill, and when the shoe was mended, Grettir went back to the den, well pleased to have enough room there for himself. He slipped the sword-knot over his wrist and walked up to the lair; the bear saw him coming, one man alone, and going out, it reared itself up and came to meet him fiercely. It struck with one paw, as a

bear will, boxing; but Grettir smote
with his sword and cut off the paw.
Then it lurched upon him trying to
bite, but Grettir dropped the sword
and seized the bear by the ears, to
hold it off. That was the hardest
trial of strength that he had yet met,
but it did not last long, for the path
was narrow and they both fell off,
over the cliff. It was a long fall and
they clung together, but the bear was
undermost, and fell upon sharp rocks
that broke his bones and pierced his
body. Then as the bear lay, still
struggling, Grettir took the sword that
hung at his wrist and slew the beast.
After that he climbed again to the den;
and taking his cloak and the paw of
the bear he walked back to Thorkel's
house.

Thorkel sat there drinking with his

men, and as Grettir came in they all laughed at him and his tattered cloak.

"The bear had left the den!" cried Biorn.

But Grettir threw down on the table the bear's paw, and they ceased laughing and began to marvel.

Then Thorkel said: "See now, Biorn, how thy jests have turned against thyself. Now I ask thee to make Grettir some atonement for his cloak."

Biorn said he would do nothing to please Grettir.

Grettir sang:

"Please or displease me as thou wilt.
    Yet if displeased must blood be spilt."

"Now," said Thorkel, "if only you two will be friends, I will pay Grettir the price of a man."

But Biorn would have no money

paid for him, and said he would run his own risks, and win or lose from Grettir as he could. Thorkel begged Grettir to do nothing against Biorn while they two lived in his house, and Grettir promised that. So they lived together the rest of the winter in Thorkel's house, and in the spring went different ways, Grettir to Norway and Biorn to England.

But in the summer, at the island of Gartar in Drontheim-firth, many ships came together and their crews went on shore, and there Grettir met Biorn. Those two took up their old quarrel, and they did not part before Biorn lay dead.

His men went home and told Thorkel, and he said that was only to be expected as soon as those two met. But Grettir went to Thorfinn of Haram-

sey and told what had happened, and
Thorfinn was glad, since now Grettir
was in need of his help.

At that time Earl Swein held the
rule over Norway, in place of his
brother Earl Eric. News came to
Swein of the slaying of Biorn, and the
news came also to Hiarandi, Biorn's
brother, who was of the Earl's body-
guard. He went before the Earl and
asked his help, and the Earl summoned
Thorfinn and Grettir to come before
him.

This they did willingly, and came
before the Earl in Drontheim. There
Thorfinn spoke of Grettir's great ser-
vices in ridding the land of the baresarks; and he told how Biorn had in
many ways offended against Grettir.
The Earl listened to that, and when
Thorfinn offered to atone Hiarandi

for the death of Biorn, the Earl backed him. But Hiarandi would take no money for the death of his brother, and so nothing came of the meeting.

Hiarandi declared he would either die or avenge his brother, so Thorfinn had his kinsman Arnbiorn go about with Grettir, wherever he went. Now one day as those two were walking in the town, a man with an axe rushed out of a gate and hewed at Grettir. Grettir did not notice, and was walking on, when Arnbiorn thrust him forward so hard that he all but fell. The axe cut along his shoulder and slashed him badly. Grettir turned, drawing his sword, and saw that it was Hiarandi who had struck him, and who now was raising the axe for another blow. Grettir struck at him, and needed not to strike again, for the blow took off his arm at the shoulder, and there he bled to death. Then five followers of Hiarandi rushed out and set upon Grettir and Arnbiorn, but those two slew four of them, and only one escaped to carry the news to the Earl.

Then there was a great to-do, for the Earl called a council. But Grettir went before it, and justified himself, since he fought to save his life. Thorfinn offered to pay the blood-fine, but the Earl would not take that, for Biorn and Hiarandi had a brother named Gunnar, and he must accept the atonement. So Grettir stayed with Thorfinn that winter, and in the spring the Earl summoned him to Tunsberg, where Gunnar dwelt.

Thorfinn and Grettir went to Tunsberg, and there Grettir found his half-brother, Thorstein Dromund, who lived there in the town. Thorstein welcomed him well, and took him in to dwell with him, but bade him beware of himself against Gunnar, who had sworn to have his life. So until the Earl should call a meeting for the atonement Grettir went about quietly, and took care not to put himself in Gunnar's way.

But one day as Grettir sat eating in a house, the door was burst in and four men rushed upon him to take his life. Grettir seized up sword and shield, and set himself in the corner, and let them come against him, Gunnar and his three men. But they could not wound him, and soon he slew one of them; then he came out of his corner and slew another. Then Gunnar and the other man wished to get away, but the man stumbled and

fell at the threshold.   Then when Gunnar was warding himself with his
shield and backing through the door,
Grettir leaped up on the beam by
the door and struck down at him
behind his shield. Both hands were
cut off, and the shield fell; then
Grettir leaped down and slew Gunnar.
But the man got away and ran to tell
the Earl.

The Earl was furiously angry, and
called a Thing to decide upon this
matter. Grettir came before it, and
with him were Thorfinn, and Thorstein Dromund, and a friend to Grettir
named Bessi; and they all had their
men with them. The Earl threatened
Grettir's life.

Then first Thorfinn went before him,
and offered to pay for all Grettir's
man-slayings. But the Earl answered

that Grettir's crimes were too great to
be atoned.

Then Bessi went before the Earl,
and offered payment, and said that the
Earl himself should say what the fines
should be. But the Earl answered
that he would not so easily forgive
Grettir his misdeeds.

Then Thorstein Dromund stepped before the Earl, and offered money, and
spoke well for Grettir. Asked the Earl:
"Why dost thou meddle in this matter?"

"Because I am his brother," answered Thorstein.

"I did not know that," answered the
Earl, "and it is right of thee to seek
to save him. Still, my mind is made
up, and I will have Grettir's life."
Then he broke up the Thing, and would
let no more be said in Grettir's favor.
He got up and went away, and Thor-

finn and Bessi and their men went with Thorstein to his house, to defend Grettir against whatever might happen.

Then the Earl armed his men and set them in array, and went with them to Thorstein's court. Those within came to the gate of the court, and the leaders went outside with Grettir, and once more they made good offers to the Earl. The Earl would not listen, and bade them give up Grettir.

They answered that if he wanted Grettir he would have to take him. So he bade his men set on, and swords were drawn and the fight had all but begun. But then came many men of substance, citizens of the town, or lords, and came between the two parties, and begged the Earl to consider wherein lay the best good of the realm, that this feud should be atoned or that many more men should be slain. Then the Earl listened, and at last they came to an agreement that fines should be paid, and that Grettir should go away out of Norway.

Said Grettir to Thorfinn when all this was settled: "Now hast thou well repaid me for my slaying of the baresarks. And thou hast won thyself fame for so withstanding the Earl." Grettir parted tenderly with Thorstein his brother, and went with Thorfinn to Haramsey, and thence he took ship for Iceland, for now his three winters of outlawry were over.

In Iceland he found that his fame had come before him and every one welcomed him. But he found it dull there in peace until he heard of a deed that he could do, which was likely to prove his strength.

CHAPTER IV

THE HAUNTINGS AT THORHALLSTEAD

A MAN named Thorhall lived at Thorhallstead in Shady-vale of Waterdale. He had a large farm and much live-stock, but the place was haunted by a troll; cattle were taken away, and men were hurt, and the shepherds and cowherds were so frightened that they would not stay. So the place got a bad name, and Thorhall could get few men to serve him; those who came stayed but a little while, except one old cowherd that worked about the barns.

At last one summer at the Althing Thorhall went to Skapti the Lawman and asked what he should do for a shepherd. "Well," answered Skapti, "I will send thee a shepherd named Glam, a Swede who will not mind thy troll; but I warn thee that he is an uncouth fellow, and not likable."

Thorhall answered that he would not mind that, if only the man would stay by him. Then Skapti sent Glam to make the bargain with Thorhall. Glam was a huge unkempt man, with a shock of hair and great gray staring eyes, uncanny to look on.

Thorhall asked, "Wilt thou watch my sheep in winter?"

Glam said he would if he were pleased with the service and not crossed in his ways; he asked what the place was like. Thorhall answered that the vale was haunted, and sometimes the shepherds were hurt.

"I do not mind such little things," said Glam. "It will be less stupid for me."

"Well," replied Thorhall, "I need such a man as thou."

So they agreed on the terms, and Glam was to come at the beginning of winter, when the hauntings increased, for they were always less in summer. Thorhall went home from the Althing, and thanked Skapti for his help, and saw nothing of Glam until the beginning of winter, but on the appointed day he came to the stead.

Thorhall welcomed him, and he took up his work well. He was out in any weather, and brought all his sheep home at evening. He would speak with the goodman, but little with the others, and they liked him little. To the women he spoke roughly, and laughed when they sang pious songs, and scoffed when he saw them going to church; a rough and savage brute of a man, was he, and but that he did the work as no one had before, he would have been sent away.

So the winter came on, and Glam lost none of his sheep, and when they asked him if he saw any strange sights he laughed, and said there had been little to notice. Then it came to the day before Christmas, and at breakfast Glam called for his meat.

"This is a fast-day," said the good-wife, "for to-morrow is Yule-day."

"I am sick and tired of such fooleries," said Glam, "and I see no way in which we are better off than when we were heathen. Now give me my meat, and stop this nonsense."

Said she: "If thou keepest not the

fast, I know it will be an unlucky day for thee."

"Bring me my food," said he, "before I make thee."

So she brought meat for very fear of him, and he ate his meal and went muttering to his work. It was a stormy day, and men could not see far on the mountain side; they heard for a while how Glam whooped to his sheep to keep them together, and as the storm grew worse they looked to have him bring the flock home early, but he did not come. They went to church, and then night drew on, and still Glam was away. Then they asked whether they should not go out to seek for him and the sheep, but it was so late and stormy that no one went.

But in the morning, when the weather was clear and all had been to church,

Thorhall sent his men out to look for Glam and the sheep. Part of the sheep they found here and part there, some in the valley and some on the hills, till all were gathered together. Then the searchers came on a place which was trampled as if men had fought there, and there the feet of the fighters had moved great stones and hacked the frozen earth. And a little way from there lay Glam dead — a fearful sight he was, black in the face and as huge as an ox.

From that fighting place there led bloody footsteps, great and shapeless, away through the snow to cliffs above the valley, and the men were afraid to venture among the rocks to see what had made those marks. But it is true that since that time the troll that had killed Glam was never seen again, so that Glam must have been the death of him.

Now, though the searchers shuddered at the sight of Glam, looking more hateful in death than he had ever been in life, they tried to bring his body to the churchyard. But he was so heavy that they could not carry him far, and so went home, for night was coming on. In the morning they went with horses and a sledge, but even then they could get him but a little way. The horses could scarcely budge the sledge, and at last they got so frightened of their burden that it was not safe to handle them, and so they were driven home.

Then on the next day the men went with the priest, who should exorcise the evil power that kept Glam from the church. But they could find the body nowhere, and at last the priest went home; and then the others found the body just where they had left it. So they took counsel with Thorhall, and at last buried Glam where he lay, with a cairn of stones over him to keep him quiet.

But soon after men came running into Thorhallstead at dusk, and said they had seen Glam walking on the hillside. Then on other days he was seen, and he was heard whooping up the valley, as if to call his sheep. He was seen close at hand by Yule-tide farers, and one man lost his wits at the sight, for the thrall was more big and fearsome than he had been in life. Then after Twelfth-night Glam was seen close by the outbuildings of the farm.

The serving men and women be-

came frightened at that, for the troll
had scarcely ever let himself be seen,
but Glam's boldness meant much evil.
So some fled away, and only the
bravest remained.

At last one night there was a great
creaking of the roof, and all knew that
Glam was walking on it; he stamped
so that they thought he would come
through the thatch. After that he
walked the roof nearly every night, and
still others of the household fled from
the place. Glam became so bold that
at last he was seen at earliest dusk,
and almost until sunrise in the morning. Those that went up into the vale
he chased, so that men scarcely ven-
tured there, even by day. It was
feared that the whole business of the
farm would go to ruin, but as spring
came on Glam was seen less, so that

Thorhall knew he should have relief from the hauntings, while summer lasted.

So Thorhall hired servants to stay with him for the summer, and it was hard to get them even for that season. He heard of a man who was looking for work, being just landed and without the money, so Thorhall went to him and offered him work. The man's name was Thorgaut; he said he was not particular what work he did.

"I need a shepherd," said Thorhall, "and I will not hide from thee that the place is haunted."

"No ghost has scared me yet," answered Thorgaut, and so they came to an agreement. Thorgaut went and watched Thorhall's sheep, and all went well through the summer, but when winter came then Glam was seen, and every night he came and walked the roof. Thorgaut laughed at that, and said the ghost must come indoors before he would be troubled.

"Lucky art thou," said Thorhall, "if thou dost not meet him."

"Thou art well scared of him, at any rate," said Thorgaut.   "But he comes not near me out of doors."

And though one day the shepherd's dog was found dead with its back broken, Glam did not meddle with Thorgaut, and except for his noises he made no trouble until it came to the day before Christmas. Then that morning the goodwife begged the shepherd not to go out with his sheep. For that was the day that Glam was slain, and it seemed as if on the day before Christmas ghosts and trolls might wreak, on those who came within their haunts, their wrath at Christ whose birthday was to follow.

But Thorgaut laughed, and said to the mistress: "I am not afraid of that. I shall return in spite of Glam."

So he went out with his sheep, and was not seen all day, and after sunset had not come home. They spoke of Glam's death on that day, and feared the same death had come upon the shepherd; but when Thorhall wished to go out and search, no one would go with him while it was dark. So it was not till morning that they went out and searched for the shepherd, and found the sheep scattered as before. And at Glam's cairn they found Thorgaut dead, terribly bruised and with his bones all broken.

They brought his body to the church-yard, and buried him there, and his spirit did not walk. But Glam grew worse than before, and began to slay the horses and the sheep which wandered up into the hills, and was often seen near the buildings, while every night he tramped the roof. Then all Thorhall's people fled to other places, excepting only his wife and an old cowherd that had been with them now for many years, who would not go because the work needed to be done. He was the only one that dared to go out before day, and he went early to his work, as he had always done.

But one morning when the sun was up the goodwife went out to the barn, and heard the cattle stamping and bellowing inside. She ran to the house and called her husband to see what was wrong. He found the cows so wild that he dared not go in among them;

but he looked in at the other buildings, and when he came to the hay-barn he found the cowherd lying all doubled up. Thorhall went to him and found him dead, with his back broken as if over Glam's knee.

Then Thorhall feared for his own life; he took his wife and his goods, and all the cattle that he could drive before him, and all the sheep that would follow, and went away out of the vale to a safe place. But Glam slew all the cattle and sheep that Thorhall left behind, and after that he went further down the valley and haunted there, cutting off stray sheep or cows and doing much damage. All dogs or horses that came up the valley he killed, and the hauntings grew less only when the spring came on.

Then Thorhall tried it once more,

and got a few servants, and went back to his house. All went well for the summer; but when the long nights came on, then Glam was seen again, and at the first word of him most of the servants fled away. Glam was very bold, and walked the roofs nightly, and broke down doors and gates and walls. Thorhall feared he must flee again, and men began to be troubled for all the lower valley, for Glam began to be seen upon the hillsides, peering down upon the farms.

CHAPTER V

GRETTIR HAS TO DO WITH GLAM

NOW Grettir, journeying to visit some kin of his in Waterdale, heard of the hauntings at Thorhallstead, and thought that here was something at which he might try his hand. He asked his kinsmen all about the matter. They saw his wishes, and would have kept him from the vale, for they said the family could not bear to lose such a man as Grettir had proved himself to be.

"Nevertheless," said Grettir, "I mean to go."

"Thy luck," foretold they, "will not always hold."

"Yet if Glam is not laid," answered Grettir, "he may visit you next." So nothing more was said on either side, and Grettir went to Thorhallstead.

Thorhall welcomed him well and was glad of his coming, for none came that way in those days. He asked where Grettir was bound, and Grettir said he came to spend the night there.

"Guests are rare with me," said Thorhall. "Now I warn thee that none come here without losing their horses, for Glam slays them all."

"Well," Grettir said, "I can buy plenty more." So the farmer put the horse in the barn, and made Grettir welcome in every way.

Grettir saw that the whole place was badly wrecked; there was not a door that had not been torn from its place, and the fences had been thrown down. Doors had been propped up at the house and barns, but everything else was in miserable order, and the farmer and his wife were there alone. But though there were all these signs of Glam, through the night there was neither sight nor sound of him, and when in the morning they went out to the barn, the horse was safe.

"This is the first night in a long while," said Thorhall, "that Glam has left me in peace."

"Either he will stay away longer," said Grettir, "or he will come to-night. And I will stay to see."

So Grettir stayed there another night, and slept in peace, for Glam did not walk the roof, and he left the door untouched. But when in the morning they went out to the barn, there was the horse dragged from his stall, and all his bones broken.

"Now," said Thorhall to Grettir, "flee away from this place, or Glam will slay thee next!"

"Nay," answered Grettir, "in payment for my horse I must at least have a sight of him." And though Thorhall still begged him to flee for his life, Grettir would not go.

So Grettir helped the farmer in his work about the place, and at night lay down in the hall, but the farmer went to his locked-bed. Grettir lay upon a settle, and before him was a strong beam by which he might brace himself. He wrapped himself in his cloak and went to sleep. A light was set to burn there, and the hall looked miserably battered and pillaged.

It was not yet midnight when Grettir

was waked by a great noise above his head as if the roof were falling in. He lay still and listened, and heard Glam tramping the roof, up and down the whole length of it; the rafters creaked under him, and the whole building groaned with the strain. For a long time Glam walked back and forth, and the farmer and Grettir both lay quiet, but every minute it seemed as if the roof would fall.

Then at length Grettir heard how the thrall leaped to the ground and strode to the door of the hall. With one twitch he snatched the door from its place and flung it far away; there was a moon that night, and Grettir saw how the light streamed in through the door into the passage. Then the moonlight was cut off as Glam stooped before the door and put in his head.

Enormously tall was he, and horribly large of head; the hair was wild and the eyes were great and glassy. He came into the passageway and stepped softly into the hall. There he straightened up so that his head was at the cross-beams; he held with his hands to the beam nearest the passage, and rolled his eyes, staring about the hall.

Grettir lay quiet, and the farmer cowered in his bed. Then when Glam's eyes were used to the dim light he saw Grettir lying like a bundle on the seat, and came up the hall with great silent strides to where he lay. He reached forth a long arm, and seized the cloak, and strove to pick Grettir up to see what he was.

Grettir braced himself by the beam at his foot, and Glam did not budge him. Then the ghost pulled harder, and still Grettir did not yield. A third time Glam pulled, and this time he raised Grettir from his place, but the stout cloak tore in two between them. Glam stood there stupidly peering at the cloth he held in his hand.

Then Grettir ran in upon him and seized him by the body, and tried to bend him backwards; but Glam stood stiff as a tree and Grettir could not move him. And Grettir saw that he had more on his hands than ever he had dreamed of.

Then he braced himself by the beam at his feet, but Glam gripped him and tore him away. Glam strove to break Grettir's hold about his waist, yet Grettir held fast, and tried again to throw him, but the weight was too great. Then Glam drove Grettir before him to crush him against the wall, but Grettir twisted about, and the panelling was broken as Glam lurched into it. So at last Glam put out his strength and by pushing or pulling he began to get Grettir away from the wall and toward the door.

That was a mighty wrestling, for Grettir did his utmost to save himself. He was no match for Glam in strength, but his skill was great, and he used every trick to stay the ghost, for once in the open he would have no chance. Then those two crashed back and forth across the hall, and broke before them seats and benches, and fell against the walls till the very timbers cracked. But ever Glam drew Grettir nearer the passage that led to the door, and at last he got him there.

Now Grettir fought for his very life, and tripped the thrall but could not throw him, and caught at the beams but could not keep his hold. Glam drew him along the passage, and at last made ready to bear him out the door.

Then Grettir saw that his last chance had come, and as Glam stooped to grasp him closer, all the time pulling toward the door, then Grettir suddenly rushed against him with all his strength, and drove him backward against the casing. They broke the lintel before them, and Glam's shoulders and head burst through the plate-beam and the thatch; then they both fell violently outward from the door, and down upon the ground. Glam fell upon his back and Grettir upon him, and there they lay, breathless, and gasping, and spent.

There in the moonlight Grettir for

the first time clearly saw Glam's face.
So dreadful was the sight, with those
huge eyes rolling horribly, that well-
nigh Grettir's spirit fled, and he had
no thought to save himself.

Then Glam spoke, and said: "Now
have we measured our strength, Grettir,
and now I lay my wierd on thee. Thou
hast only half the strength which
would have come to thee hadst thou
not put thyself in my way; now it shall
never grow greater, though many will
call thee strong enough. And now has
thy luck turned, and whatever thou
doest after this shall go against thee.
Thou shalt be outlawed, and wilt dwell
much alone; then often shalt thou see
my glaring eyes, and shalt dread to be
alone, and that shall be thy death."

But when Glam had finished speaking, then Grettir roused himself, and

drew his sword, and smote the ghost's head from his body, and laid it at his thigh.

Then Grettir called the farmer out, and showed him what he had done, and Thorhall praised God that his plague was gone at last. Then they made a great fire over Glam, and burnt him all to ashes, and brought those to a barren place, and buried them deep. And Glam never walked again, nor troubled any one more, save only Grettir, as will be seen.

Thorhall called his neighbors, and told what had happened, and they all praised Grettir as the bravest and strongest man that ever had come into Iceland. And Thorhall gave Grettir another horse, and new clothes, for his own were torn to shreds; and Grettir rode away to his own kin.

But always after that Grettir saw strange shapes in the dark, and all sorts of horrors disturbed his sleep, and he could scarcely bear to be alone in the night.   And often he saw before him Glam's rolling glassy eyes.

CHAPTER VI

GRETTIR COMES INTO HIS OUTLAWRY

IN those days the news came to Iceland that Olaf Haraldson, who later was called Olaf the Saint, was king in Norway, and that many stout men were flocking to him, for he received them well. When Grettir heard that he began to weary of his life at home, where all was quiet, and made ready to go to Norway to seek service with the king, who was of his distant kin. So he left his father, who now was an old man, and sailed to Norway. There he took passage in another ship, and sailed northward along the coast, to meet the king.

The season was late, and the days were short and the nights very cold. One night the sailors tried to reach a harbor, but could not, and were forced to lay up under the lee of an island. There was a wide channel between it and the mainland, and the waves were very rough. On the island was no shelter at all, and though there was wood, they had no fire, nor means to make it. The wind was bitter cold, and the men were all wet, and they feared they would freeze. Then at dark they saw over on the mainland the lights of a hall.

Then the men questioned if they dared to launch the ship and get across the sound, but the waves and the currents were too dangerous. Yet they feared for their lives where they stayed, and knew not what to do. Some of them asked if any one of them was able to swim across and fetch fire.

"There have been men," said Grettir, "who would have done that."

"That is no help to us," said they. "But thou art called the bravest and hardiest of all Icelanders now living. Couldst thou do it?"

Grettir knew that would be a great feat, but remembering the words of Glam, that what he did should turn out against him, he said: "Do it I can, but I know not how ye will reward me for it."

"Of course we will reward thee well," answered they.

"That will be seen," said Grettir. "I will fetch fire for you, and do you bear in mind this promise of yours."

So he stripped off his outer clothing and swam the sound, and a hard swim it was on account of the tide-rips, and a difficult landing he found among the rocks. Then he walked to the hall and opened the door. Now the salt spray had frozen all over his hair and beard, and his clothes froze stiff as he walked, and when he walked in among those in the hall, they started from their seats, and stared at him, thinking him a troll.

Now those were Icelanders and men of spirit, and though they thought him a monster they took courage against him, and set on him with weapons before ever he had a chance to speak. But Grettir struck their weapons from their hands with his bare arms. Then seeing how they did nothing against him with their steel, they cried that evil spirits must yield to fire, and they snatched up burning brands and torches and struck at him with those, coming at him from all sides. Then Grettir, seeing that he would get nothing from them but blows, for in their shouting they did not hear his words, seized a torch from one of them, and with it he smote himself a way among them.

That was strange fighting, for with the swinging of the torches the fire leaped over all the hall, and set fire to the straw that lay there; and soon all was fire and smoke, with the sound of blows and the shouting of men. Then though they were so fierce against him, Grettir won the door and so got away; he ran down to the shore and leaped into the sea, and began his swim back to his shipmates.

And that was almost the hardest swim that ever man has made. For first he had to get clear of the breakers, and then he had to meet the currents and the adverse winds. The waves ran high, and the tides pulled him this way and that; it would have been a great enough task to make that swim without any burden. But all the time Grettir had to hold aloft his burning torch, and to take care that no splashing wave should put it out. So he had but one arm to swim with, and that made the work very hard, and all the time the cold was deadly. Sometimes he thought he would be cast back upon the rocks, and sometimes he thought he made no headway at all. But still he struggled, till at last he saw the islet before him, and so at last he came to land.

There his shipmates seized and welcomed him, and made a fire, and warmed him. He put on dry clothes, and made little of their thanks; and soon, in the safety of their fire, they were all asleep.

But across the sound, in the hall, those Icelanders who had fought Grettir made much of themselves when they saw that he had gone. Some peered after him from the door, and saw that he threw himself into the sea; thus they were sure that he was a troll. Then they set to and put out the fires among the straw, and talked it all over, and thought they had a great tale to tell of that night's affray. And so at length they lay down and went to sleep. Yet, as it happened, there was still fire smouldering in some straw that was heaped by the wall. The fire got into the wall, and burned there for a while, until at last it got into the thatch, and burst out all over the place. The men knew nothing of it until the timbers were falling upon their heads; by that time the place was so thick with smoke that they were half smothered and could see nothing. They had barred the door, and none of them got out, but all were burned there.

Then in the morning the gale had gone down, and when Grettir and his mates launched their ship they saw that across the sound there seemed to be the smoking embers of a great fire; and they wished to know who had been so uncourteous as to set on Grettir as those men had done. So they rowed across to the mainland, and when they came on shore they saw that the hall itself had burned down; and when they came to look they found the bones of men among the embers, and there was no one there to tell the tale.

Then some of the shipmen cried out on Grettir: "Thou hast burned those men!"

"How could I burn them?" he asked. "There was no fire seen from the islet even when we went to sleep, and that was long after I was here."

But they still looked upon him with suspicion, and whispered apart.

"Now it is as I foreboded," said Grettir. "And this is how ye reward me for saving your lives."

But they had no shame, and feared only that suspicion might come upon them for burning those men. At the next harbor, when Grettir and others went on shore, they gave him the slip and sailed away northward without him, and wherever they stopped they told how Grettir had burned those men in their house. So that as Grettir also travelled northward he found men had turned against him. At last he came to Drontheim, where the king was; but the story had been told to the king, and Grettir found it hard to come before him until some days had passed. But at last he came before him where the king sat in his hall, with his men about him.

Said Grettir to the king: "An evil tale has been told against me, O king, and I wish to clear myself of it."

Then the king, who was saintly in all his ways and foresighted also, said to Grettir: "Well art thou called the Strong, but I perceive that ill luck is ever ready to follow thee. Tell me thy story."

So Grettir told his story, how those

men had set on him with firebrands, but that he had left them all alive in the hall, while for a long while afterward no fire had sprung up in the building, for it would have been seen from across the sound. Then Grettir begged the king to help him clear himself before the law.

Then the king said: "Thou mayest clear thyself by bearing hot iron in the church. And it is likely that the men were burnt by evil fortune, but thy luck may not stay with thee to prove it so."

Grettir thanked him and was pleased, for by the ordeal of bearing the glowing iron a man might clear himself from an accusation. So a day was set, and Grettir fasted until then, to make himself fit to prove his innocence. When the day came there was a great crowd by the church. The king and the bishop went inside, and Grettir came from his lodging to go to the church. The people gazed on him and wondered at his great size, and said that there was a man fit to do the things that were told of him.

So Grettir approached the church door, but before he came to it there started out from the crowd a lad of strange shape, large and with a huge head, with wild eyes and much hair. He wagged his head at Grettir and pointed at him, and he cried: —

"Fine mummery and mockery is this! And a great honor it is to Norway that this freebooter and man of violence shall thus escape from the penalty of his misdeeds! Any man is allowed to bear the iron who claims the right to do so, and so the greatest criminals escape punishment. And this man is the worst of all, for he burned helpless men, and for no cause. Now it is a great shame that he shall thus be allowed to get away scot-free."

And more words he said, standing in front of Grettir and pointing at him, and calling him evil names, such as sea-monster, and half-man — for no man, said he, could have such growth and strength. And so uncouth was he, and wild of look, that Grettir shuddered at him and hated him, and when the lad came near Grettir struck him with his fist and felled him.

Then there was shouting and pressing of the people to see what had happened, and in the press the lad disappeared. Some say he vanished away suddenly, and the truth is that no one knows more of him. It is thought he was some troll, sent there by Glam to be Grettir's undoing, for if Grettir had come into the church the evil spirits could not reach him; and if he had borne the iron he would have broken the current of his ill-fortune.

But the word was brought to the king that Grettir was in a brawl, and Olaf came out of the church and found Grettir standing looking about him for the lad, and all amazed, as if he had seen Glam himself.

"Now," said the king, "by this violence thou hast put from thyself all the virtue gained by thy fasting, and hast broken in upon the solemn ordeal. After this it will not be possible to clear thee by means of the hot iron."

Then Grettir was much cast down,

and spoke to the king of the kinship between them, and how he had made the long journey from Iceland in the hope of taking service with the king. He asked to be taken into the king's body-guard.

"Nay," answered Olaf. "None of my men is a match for thee in courage or in strength, but thy luck will bring trouble on all who are with thee, and that I cannot have."

"But how can I clear myself of this suspicion of the burning?" asked Grettir.

"In no way that I see," replied Olaf. "And because there will always be violence wherever thou art I must forbid thee to stay in this kingdom. Here mayest thou stay in peace this winter and no more; in the summer shalt thou go home to Iceland, for there thou shalt die. Many a man's hand will be against thee, for I see that an evil curse hangs over thee."

Then Grettir, much cast down, went away and saw the king no more. He thought of going to his friend Thorfinn, but it seemed as if he had brought on him trouble enough. Then he said to himself he would seek his brother in Tunsberg, and so set out by land to go there.

At Christmas time he came to the house of a farmer named Einar, who took Grettir in and treated him well. Einar was a rich man, and it was well-known that he had much goods with him in his house.

So it happened that two days after Christmas, when all Einar's Christmas-guests had gone away, excepting only Grettir, that there came out of the woods a band of men, and before them a leader on a horse, who called Einar out to speak with him.

"Now heaven help us!" said Einar to Grettir, "here is the baresark Snaekol and his men, and they will rob me of all my goods."

"Let us hold the house against him," said Grettir.

But the house was large, and those two and the house-carles could not hold it against so many, who would not scruple at setting it afire above their heads. So Einar went out to speak with the baresark, and Grettir went with him, but without arms.

The baresark sat on his horse and shouted at Einar that he should give up all his goods and his household, or else fight with him for them. Einar was old, and was no fighting man;

he whispered Grettir, asking what he
should do.

"Thou shalt do only that which is
not shameful," answered Grettir.

Then the baresark rode nearer.
"What art thou saying with that big
fellow?" he asked. "Will he perhaps
fight me?"

"I also have no skill in arms," said
Grettir.

"You are both afraid of me," cried
Snaekol.

"Thou art very terrible," answered
Grettir.

But because he did not seem to be
afraid the baresark grew angry, and
thought to cow Grettir. So he rode
closer still, gritted his teeth, and began
to howl after the manner of baresarks,
and to foam at the mouth. He opened
his mouth and thrust his shield into it,

bit the edge of the shield, and howled louder than before. Then Grettir took a step forward, and drove his foot up against the shield, so that it was dashed into the baresark's mouth, and tore out his teeth and broke his lower jaw. Then while the fellow tottered in his saddle Grettir seized him and dragged him from his horse, and drew the outlaw's short-sword, and cut off his head at a stroke.

At sight of that the baresark's followers, a mere rabble, were frightened and fled to the woods. Having lost their leader each man ran his own way, and that was the end of that band of evil-doers. This was another of Grettir's deeds in ridding lands of their pests, and he was thanked not by Einar alone, but also by all the men of that neighborhood.

Grettir went on and came to Tuns-berg, where he was welcomed gladly by his brother Thorstein Dromund, and lived with him that winter. No more deeds are told of Grettir in that season. He stayed with his brother until summer, and then made ready to take ship again for Iceland.

It happened that one morning Thorstein woke up from his sleep, and saw where Grettir lay still sleeping, with his arms thrown outside the bedclothes. Thorstein marvelled at him, and when Grettir was awake he said:

"I have been looking at thine arms, and now I know why thy blows are so heavy."

"I could not have done what I have," answered Grettir, "with smaller arms."

"Still," replied Thorstein, "it would

have been better for thee had they been smaller and luckier."

"It happens to each according to his fate," said Grettir. "Now show me thine arms." And when he had seen them he laughed and said: "Why, thou art a very spindle, and thine arms are tongs! Thou hast scarcely the strength of a woman." For Thorstein was indeed one of the leanest of men.

"Well," answered Thorstein, "this I foresee, that either my thin arms shall avenge thee, or thou shalt lie un-avenged."

And that came true, as later will appear. When Grettir sailed, the brothers parted with love, and they never saw each other again.

But in Iceland that summer, at the Althing, before Grettir came to land, a suit was brought against him by Thorir of Garth, the father of two of those who had been burned in that house from which Grettir fetched the fire. Now Grettir's kinsmen had heard nothing of this, and they were not ready for the suit. They tried to postpone it until he should come and defend himself; but Thorir pressed the case so hard, and had so many men of influence to back him, that he made Grettir an outlaw throughout Iceland, Many said it was done unlawfully, but it was done for all that.

CHAPTER VII

GRETTIR MUST REMAIN AN OUTLAW

WHEN Grettir landed in Iceland he was met by bad news, for first he learned that his father was dead, and next that he was outlawed and that a price was set upon him. And last he was told that just before he landed his brother had been slain by a neighbor, who now was trying to get Grettir's mother from her farm.

This is the story of the slaying of Atli, the brother of Grettir. He was in no way like his brother, for he was slow and good-natured, gentle and peace-loving. But because he was prosperous and much loved, there were also some who envied him, and they sought to get the better of him. Atli had a neighbor, Thorbiorn, a man of great strength, and so called Oxmain. This man egged two of his kinsmen on to slay Atli; but Atli, although he had never fought before, slew the both with the sword which Grettir had given him, the sword of his great-grandfather.

Thorbiorn Oxmain brought suit against Atli for the slaying of his kinsmen, but got little satisfaction save small fines, and that only made him eager for vengeance. Now one winter a workman of his ran away and went to Atli, who took him in and gave him work. Then in his anger Thobiorn went one day to the house of Atli, got him to the door by a trick, and stabbed him with a great spear. No vengeance was taken for that by Grettir's kinsmen, for they waited to see what Grettir would do when he came to land.

So Grettir was told all that news, which might have overwhelmed a common man. But it seemed to him no worse than other evil luck which had come upon him, so he laughed, and sang:

> "Mournful is the news I hear:
> Dead are both my kinsmen dear;
> Outlaw have I just been made.
> I should therefore be afraid.
> — But there may be one or two
> Who shall soon my coming rue."

And that night, before his shipmates suspected, he stole away from them, and by various paths crossed the hills to his own homestead of Biarg, and so chose his time that he came there at night, when all folk were asleep. He went into the hall by a secret way, and came to his mother's locked bed, and waked her up by taking her hand.

"Who is there?" she asked.

"It is thy son Grettir," answered he.

Then she sat up and kissed him, but with tears; and she welcomed him, but sadly. "For thy life is in danger," she said, "and thy brother's enemy presses upon me to drive me from this house, and thy brother Illugi cannot help me for many years, since he is but three years old."

"Be of better heart," said Grettir. "For it may chance that my brother's enemy will not trouble thee much longer. Truly my luck is bad, but it may serve me so far as to get me to meet him, and after that his luck must be great indeed if he gets away from

me. For he who is struck will strike
in return, and that is known of me
already."

Then Grettir stayed there a day or
two in secret, and sent a man over the
ridge to see whether Thorbiorn Oxmain was at home. The man came
back and said that Thorbiorn was at
home with few men, working at his
haying. Then on a bright morning
Grettir rode over the ridge to Thorbiorn's house, and came there at mid-
day. The women came to the door
at his knock, and did not know him.
They said that the master had gone
to his meadow for hay, and his son
was with him. So Grettir rode along
the way they showed him, and when
he came to the meadow and saw Thorbiorn working on the hillside above
him, he came down from his horse,

and looked to his weapons. He had his short-sword and his helmet, with a large spear, of which the head was inlaid with silver.

He saw how Thorbiorn and his son had stopped working and were looking at him. Their arms were close at hand: Thorbiorn had a shield and sword, and his son, Arnor, had a small axe. The lad was sixteen years old, but well grown. With them a woman had been working, raking the hay.

When Grettir saw how those two were armed, he sat down and knocked out of his spear the nail that held the head, so that, the spear once thrown, it would not be of use for Thorbiorn to throw it back.

"See what he is doing," said Thorbiorn to his son. "He comes against

So They Took up Their Arms and Made Ready

us to fight, and from his size he must be Grettir the Strong. But come," and he spoke to hearten the lad, "remember I am called Oxmain for my own strength, and we are two to one. This is what we will do: I will undertake to hold my own against him for a while, and while I keep him busy do thou come at him from behind, and hew at his back. Be not afraid; he will have his hands so full with me that he will not harm thee."

So they took up their arms and made ready, although neither of them had a helmet. Grettir came up the slope against them, having knocked the nail out of his spear. When he was near enough, he cast the spear at Thorbiorn, but the head was so loose that it came off, and the spear turned aside and did no harm. Then Thorbiorn

and his son separated, so that Arnor
could come at Grettir from behind.

Grettir, when he saw their plan, did
not let Thorbiorn come to close fighting, as he wished, but fought away
from him, and scarcely kept within
reach, while he watched to see what
Arnor was doing. But when the lad
thought he had a good chance, then he
ran in against Grettir, with his axe
lifted with both hands, to hew Grettir's backbone in two. Then Grettir
swung round upon him with a back-
handed blow, and cleft his skull at a
stroke.

Just as he stood still to do that,
Thorbiorn ran at him from in front,
and struck mightily. But Grettir
turned the blow with his shield, and
having his arm already drawn back
by the blow at Arnor, now he slashed

forward with such a stroke that he
split Thorbiorn's shield, and the sword
passed on into Thorbiorn's head and
killed him at once. So with those
two strokes Grettir got full vengeance
for his brother.

The woman who was there ran home
shrieking, and told of the deed. Those
at the house gathered men, but when
they came to the meadow Grettir had
gone. He stayed long enough to look
for his spear-head, but could not find
it. (Now it was found in the time of
Sturla the Lawman, after more than
two hundred years, in the field called
Spearmead.) Grettir rode to the nearest
house, and told of the slayings; then
he rode home and told his mother.

"Well," said she, "now all may see
how safe it is to anger thee. But soon
they will be here with all their men,

and because thou art an outlaw it is against the law for any one to defend thee, so thou must away."

Grettir went away, therefore, but first he told his kinsmen of his deed, and they promised to help him in whatever way they might. After he had gone came the relatives of Thorbiorn Oxmain, his brother at their head. They asked if Grettir were hidden away there.

"Thou shouldst know by what has just happened," answered Grettir's mother, "if he is a man to hide. Now thou canst do thy best against him, but he is not here."

They went home with only their journey for their pains, and in the meantime Grettir went west, to Snorri the Priest. He was the wisest man in all Iceland in matters of craft, and was bound to Grettir's family by old ties of friendship, but he was well on in years. Grettir laid his case before Snorri, and begged advice, and asked him to take him under his care.

"I cannot take thee in," said Snorri, "for I care not to go against the law. But when thy case comes up before the Althing again, then I will go with thy family to help them, for I think I see a flaw in the suit against thee which may help thee out of thine out-lawry."

So Grettir went away, but when those cases came before the courts at the next Althing, then Snorri the Priest was there to listen. There were two suits that were brought forward, one for the slaying of Atli, in which Grettir was made the suitor for the death of his brother; and one for the slaying of Thorbiorn Oxmain. Then the judges were about to set the cases off against each other, so that there should be nothing to pay on either side. Then the lawman asked (and he was of Grettir's kin) how it was possible to do that.

The judges said, because Atli and Thorbiorn were men of equal standing.

"But," answered the lawman, Skapti Thorod's son, "Grettir can come into neither of these suits, for at the time of both slayings he was an outlaw, and no outlaw can come into a suit at law. Thorbiorn's kinsmen cannot sue Grettir for the slaying, but Atli's kinsmen can sue against the kin of Thorbiorn," — and so all saw that Atli's nephews could sue for payment for his slaying; while in the case of Thorbiorn it was as if no one had slain him, Grettir

being an outlaw, with no one account-
able for his deeds. So Thorbiorn's kin
would have to pay a fine, but Atli's
kin would not.

Then Snorri the Priest came forward, and he said: "Will not Grettir's
kin drop their suit for the slaying of
Atli, if only Grettir can be thus got out
of his outlawry?"

Both sides agreed to that, and so it
was all arranged, except for one thing,
the consent of Thorir of Garth, at
whose suit for the burning of his sons
Grettir had been made outlaw. So
Thorir of Garth was sent for, and his
consent was asked.

But Thorir turned away in bitter
anger, and said that Grettir should
never be brought out of his outlawry,
save only by death.

"This will be a heavy thing for Iceland, to keep Grettir in his outlawry for a deed that has never been proved against him," said Snorri the Priest. "And many a man will rue it."

But Thorir of Garth was not to be moved, and so the whole matter fell to the ground. Thorir raised the price on Grettir's head to three marks of silver; and the kinsmen of Thorbiorn Oxmain, in wrath that they had to pay a fine for Atli's slaying, set another three marks on Grettir's head. And this was considered very wonderful, for never before had more than three marks been set on any outlaw.

So Grettir remained an outlawed man, and it was long before it was again tried to get him free from the ban. But because of the injustice of his outlawry he refused to leave Iceland, and never went abroad again.

CHAPTER VIII

GRETTIR IN OUTLAWRY

THE first winter of Grettir's outlawry he spent with one named
Thorgils, at Reekness; it was out of
the country of Grettir's foes, and Thorgils was a great harborer of outlaws.
When Grettir came to him Thorgils
said he would take him in if only he
would keep the peace. "But," said
Thorgils, "there are here two foster-
brothers, kinsmen of mine, who are
both unruly men and afraid of little."

Grettir said he was never the man
to begin a quarrel — and this is true
of him, that in all his slayings he was
not the raiser of trouble, and when-

ever he struck he first gave warning. So Thorgils took him in, and with the foster-brothers, Thorgeir and Thormod, Grettir lived together in the same house in peace, strifeful men as they all were. Thormod and Grettir were good friends, but Thorgeir bore himself sourly toward Grettir.

Now Thorgils owned islands off the coast, and on one of them was an ox that had been fattened for Christmas, and the farmer wished it fetched ashore. So one day those foster-brothers, men of great strength, said they would go and fetch the ox if a third would go with them in the ten-oared boat. Grettir said he would go, and so they started, three in the boat that usually needed eleven men, ten to row and one to steer. It was a cold day, with the wind high and the water rough

When they reached the island there was no sheltered place to land or to draw up their boat, so they went ashore in the surf. Grettir gave them their choice, either to hold the boat or to fetch the ox; they chose to fetch the ox, and Grettir stood there in the surf to hold the boat while they were gone. The water was ice-cold, and the spray froze on him and in the boat; sometimes the waves rose to his neck, yet he held the boat in its place and kept it from the rocks. Then after a time the foster-brothers came back with the ox, and put it in the boat, and they started to row back.

Thormod rowed forward in the boat, Thorgeir amidships, and Grettir in the stern; they did well till they were in the broadest part of the bay, when a squall struck them, and they labored against it and scarcely got forward at all. Thorgeir said that Grettir was not doing his share of the work.

"I am doing mine," said Grettir, "but I am not doing thine."

Then Thorgeir rowed so hard that he broke his tholepins and had to stop to mend them. When he began again Grettir's oars were worn so thin that they broke in two.

"More haste the worse speed," said Thormod, who rowed steadily and broke neither oars nor pins.

Now there were in the boat two rough-hewn beams that were to be made into oars. These Grettir took, and struck them through the boat below the gunwales, and rowed so powerfully that at last the boat reached shore. Then he asked the foster-brothers whether they would lead the ox home or haul up the boat, and again they chose the lighter task and said they would haul up the boat. So they hauled it up, heavy with water as it was, and all caked with ice. Grettir started on ahead with the ox, but the beast was so fat, and was so unused to walking, that at last it got tired and would not go on.

The foster-brothers came along the path, but would not help Grettir with his task, since they had finished theirs. They went on to the house, and told where Grettir was, and then they waited a while; but then some one called that there was a great sight coming, and they saw Grettir, with the ox on his shoulders. He brought it right up to the house, and all were amazed at him.

Thorgeir got so jealous of Grettir's

strength and fame, that one day, after Grettir had been to bathe, Thorgeir met him in the path, bearing an axe on his shoulder. "I hear," said Thorgeir, "that thou hast said thou wouldst never give way to one man."

"I may have said it," replied Grettir, "and I have not yet given way to thee."

Then Thorgeir swung up the axe, but Grettir ran in upon him and threw him down before he could strike. Thorgeir called for help to Thormod who stood by; but Thormod could do nothing with Grettir, and was about to draw his sword when the farmer came up and bade them be quiet; they obeyed him, making out that it was all a jest.

There are no more tales told of that winter, except that once when the farmer was asked which was the bravest of those three he answered: "Two of them know fear, for Thormod fears God, and Grettir sees such shapes in the dark that he will never go out at night unless he must. But Thorgeir seems not to know what fear is."

That was Grettir's last winter in a house with other men, for in the spring his enemies learned that he was with Thorgils, and sent a band to kill him; but he had gone before they came. Then Thorgils was threatened with the law for harboring Grettir, and so would never take him in again. Thorgils got much fame because he had kept those three unruly men a whole winter in his house, and made them keep the peace; but no one after him was ever willing to take Grettir in, except only for a few days at a time.

Grettir, when he went away in the

spring, went into the Icefirth dales, and went about openly and carelessly, taking from the people whatever he wished, for none of them dared resist him singly. But he was so reckless, taking no pains to hide himself, that at last they planned to go against him at a place where he slept, and finding him asleep they cast ropes on him, and after a struggle they bound him and tied him to a tree.

These men were small tenants, and Grettir felt it a great shame that they should get the better of him. Then before his face they talked over how they should dispose of him, and how to get the reward for him. They said that one of them should keep him until they could send for Grettir's foes.

But that man said he had enough to do besides guarding a man like Grettir.

with whom a man's life would never be safe.

Then they offered Grettir to the next man, and to the next, offering each a double share of the head-money, but each man begged off like the first, for dread of Grettir. So at last they decided to hang him there and then, and so get the money just the same. They began to make a gibbet on which to hang him.

But just then rode along, on the hillside below, the wife of the chief of those parts; she was a large woman, called Thorbiorg the Big, wife of Vermund the Slender. When she saw that there was something going on upon the hillside she left her horse and went thither, and found Grettir there tied, and the men making ready to hang him. They were all her husband's men, and gave Grettir into her hands willingly enough, when she asked it, telling them that to hang Grettir was too bold a thing for them to dare to do. Then she asked of Grettir: "Why wert thou here robbing my men?"

"I must be somewhere," he answered.

"That is so," she said. "But if I give thee thy life wilt thou take no revenge for thy capture, and never ravage in these dales again?"

He promised that readily, and she let him go, and she was renowned for the act ever afterward. Grettir got himself away from Icefirth, and never came there again.

So now he had learned caution, and never again, in whatever place he slept, were men able to come upon him unawares. But because no one would take him in, and because he was tired of robbing folk, he went to Ernewater Heath and built himself a hut in a strong place. He made himself a boat and nets, and lived on the fish he caught in the lakes; but the mountains there were so wild and lonely, and he saw such things in the dark, that the life was hateful to him.

The word went round that Grettir was somewhere in that region, so his enemies got a man named Grim, an outlaw, to go and offer himself to live with Grettir, promising that for slaying Grettir they would get Grim out of his outlawry and pay him much money. So Grim went till he found Grettir, and begged to be allowed to live with him, for both of them were outlaws.

"I hate it so much here alone" said Grettir, "that I will take thee in, if thou wilt do what work I require."

Grim said he would like nothing better, and so he lived there with Grettir for nearly the whole of the winter, always watching for a chance to slay him. But Grettir was so wary that there never was any chance; he kept his weapons with him by day, and by night he hung his short-sword over his head.

But one day Grim went out early to fish, and Grettir lay abed, and was still there when Grim returned. Grim made a noise of stamping, but Grettir lay quiet, and did not move.

Then Grim was sure he was asleep; and after he had made more noise, while Grettir did not stir, he went stealthily to the bed, and took down the short-sword, and drew it. But as he raised it to strike, Grettir sprang from the bed, for he had only been shamming. He threw Grim on the ground, and made him tell how it all had been planned, and then slew him. Then Grettir lived there alone the rest of the winter and all the summer, but the life was very wearisome.

Now his enemies got another outlaw, Thorir Redbeard, to try the same thing against Grettir. He was unwilling to venture at first, but they talked him into it, and promised him much. So he went to Ernewater Heath by a roundabout way, lest Grettir should suspect him, and when he met him begged to be taken in.

Said Grettir, "A man came here a year ago, and when I had taken him in he tried to slay me foully. I want no more such men as he."

But Thorir spoke fairly, making many promises, so that at last Grettir made up his mind to risk it, and thus be rid of his loneliness. Thorir was the most willing of workers, doing whatever Grettir wished, so that Grettir's life was now very easy. But he was always so watchful that Thorir never got any chance at him. They lived there two winters in that lonely spot, and Thorir never found a moment when he could catch Grettir off his guard.

But in the second spring there came a storm, and when Grettir in the early morning woke and asked if their boat was safe, Thorir planned what he could do. He went down to the shore, where they kept their boat by a point of land that went straight down into the water on one side, and on the other had a beach. Thorir broke the boat to pieces, and went back and told Grettir that the storm had ruined it.

"And," said he, "the nets are still out in the water, and they will be spoiled if they are driven ashore."

"This is all thy fault," said Grettir. "Thou shouldst last night have pulled the boat up on the beach and brought the nets ashore. Go now and bring them in."

"But I cannot swim," said Thorir. "Thou knowest that I am willing enough to work, but this is beyond me."

So Grettir rose and took his sword, and went down to the point, where sure enough the nets were in danger. Again he bade Thorir go and get them, but he said he could not, and asked

Grettir why he was afraid to do it himself.

"I will do it," said Grettir, "and my life is in thy hands."

"I will not betray thee," replied Redbeard.

Grettir took off his clothes and laid aside his sword, and swam out to the nets. He brought them ashore where the shore was steep, but just as he himself was climbing up Thorir snatched up the sword and drew it, and leaped at Grettir to slay him. Then Grettir fell right down backwards into the water and sank out of sight; he turned and swam under water close to the shore, and did not come up until he had turned the point, but all the time Thorir stood there watching for him to come up. Grettir got ashore, and crept softly up behind Thorir, who still stood gazing into the water, hearing nothing until Grettir picked him up and dashed him down on the ground, so that he dropped the sword. Grettir waited to get no story from him, but slew him there and then.

Then once more he was alone, but he liked his life no better than before.

CHAPTER IX

GRETTIR AND HALLMUND

TIME hung so heavily on Grettir's hands that summer that at last he went forth again, leaving the lonely heath and coming once more near the abodes of men. His clothes were rags, and he needed many things for his housekeeping there on the heath. So one day, as he lay on a hillside and saw going along below him a man on a horse, leading another loaded with goods, he said to himself: "That man has too much for his needs, and I have too little for mine; so I will have to do with him."

He went down from his lair and

stood in the man's way. Now the man was very large of growth, well dressed in colored clothes, and the fittings of his horse's harness were curiously worked. He had on his head a hat with a wide brim, pulled down over his brow, so that in their dealings Grettir did not once have a clear sight of his face. Grettir called on him to halt, and asked his name.

"My name is Air," said the man, in a great voice, "and I know thee for Grettir Asmund's son. What can I do for thee?"

"Thou canst give me some of thy goods," answered Grettir, "for my clothes are falling off my back for age."

"What wilt thou pay me?" asked Air.

"If thou knowest my name," said

Grettir, "thou knowest also that I never pay for what I take."

"Take what thou canst where thou canst," replied Air. "But as for me, I am riding on." And he urged on his horse, but Grettir caught it by the bridle with both hands.

"Stop with me a while," said Grettir. But Air, without words, reached with his long arms down before Grettir's hands, and took hold of the reins between them and the bit. Then he drew the reins to him and away from Grettir, and though Grettir gripped his best, the reins were dragged right away from him. Then Air rode on again.

Grettir looked at his hands, and saw how the leather had cut them. Then he marvelled at the man's strength, for no man before now had ever got the

better of him — no, nor troll either.
He asked of the man, "Where art thou
going?"

Air stopped and sang:

> "Among the hills
> And the mountain rills.
> If thou wilt come
> To seek my home,
> Stone land of fist
> Is the place, I wist."

"If I am to find it I must know
clearer than that," said Grettir.

Then Air sang again:

> "If thou wouldst know
> The place to go,
> On Ball-jokul's side
> Do I abide."

And with that he rode on and away,
and left Grettir standing there. Now
Grettir knew that Ball-jokul was not

far from his hut on Ernewater Heath, but it was a mountain, bare and icy, and no man lived there. So he wondered who this Air could be, with his size and strength, and such a voice. A little fear came over him, and he looked again after Air, and saw that he had vanished clean away. Then Grettir shuddered to himself, and marvelled more, and sang this song:

"Now am I too small, alone,
    To match this wight from land of stone.
    And maidens all will laugh to hear
    Before him Grettir shrank in fear."

Then he too went on his way, and managed to get himself fresh clothes and new fittings, and so went back to his hut on the heath to dwell there another winter, although he loathed it. Now Thorir of Garth, who had sent,

Thorir Redbeard against Grettir, learned that Grettir had again been seen abroad, and so was sure that Redbeard was slain. And meaning this time not to fail, he gathered a band of nearly eighty men, and rode with them to find Grettir's fastness on the heath. Then one day, as Grettir was on a hillside, he saw men coming, a great band of them, who had already seen him. He was so glad of a change in his life that he would not run from them, but took his stand in the strongest place he could find, and that was not strong enough. For though when men came at him in front they must come between rocks, one at a time, they could also get at him from the rear, and he would have hard work to defend himself, if they were his foes. That he found out soon enough, when he saw Thorir of Garth at the head of them.

Now Thorir was past the prime of life, and not a fighting man. So he stayed on his horse behind his men, but bade them dismount and slay Grettir. "For now," he cried, "we have him where he cannot escape."

"There's many a slip twixt cup and lip," said Grettir, "and I shall set my mark on some of you first."

Then they set on Grettir from in front, and he had plenty to do in warding himself, while he heard Thorir sending others round to take him from behind. It was an ill place for fighting, and the work was hard; ever as he felled a man the man would be dragged away, and the others would come on freshly, with good courage. He had no moment of rest, and before long he was weary, so hot was that bout; and all the time he listened to hear the footsteps of men behind him, in the rocky passage. Grettir was wounded, and bled somewhat, and thought soon to meet his death.

But however many men Thorir might send to Grettir's back, they fell before they got to him, with great wounds, nor was there any one visible to deal such strokes. Many fell before Grettir, some dead and some wounded; but more fell in the passage behind him, till the men of Thorir were frightened and refused to go on with the onslaught.

Then said Thorir himself: "We have always known that Grettir is above all other men in might, but now I see he is a wizard, leagued with evil powers. There are trolls fighting against us, and now let us flee away!"

So they drew off, and in good time for Grettir, for he was almost spent. Eighteen men lay there dead when Thorir rode away, and many rode home with great wounds.

Grettir stood there marvelling. He had heard behind him the groans of dying men, and now as he stood there, getting his breath, he heard some one breathing heavily in the passage of the rocks. So when Grettir was rested he went into the passage, and found sitting there a huge man, much wounded, who leaned against the rock. Beyond him lay the bodies of twelve men whom he had slain, but Grettir had killed only six.

"Thou hast saved me," said Grettir. "But who art thou?"

"My name is Hallmund," said the wounded man, "and I am he who met thee last summer and pulled his reins from thy hands; now perhaps I have paid thee for my roughness."

"In truth thou hast," said Grettir, "and when I can, I will repay thee. Now let me bind up thy wound."

"Nay," said the big man, "my home is not far, and the wound will soon heal. Come with me and leave this place, for it must be irksome here."

So Grettir went with him, and on the side of Ball-jokul they found a cave. There was a woman of large size; she was Hallmund's daughter, and she bound up the wounds of both of them, so that they healed well. Now Grettir saw that these two were different from human folk, both in their size and in their living in that manner in the mountain, where no man had ever seen a cave. So he knew that they were earth-spirits friendly to man. And that "stone land of fist" which Hallmund had called his dwelling was really a play upon his own name, which translates into those words.

Grettir dwelt with those two for a while, and they treated him well. They had deep knowledge of hidden things, and were wise and far-sighted. Grettir and Hallmund had sport together, and made rhymes upon each other and upon their fight with Thorir's men; but in the end Grettir grew restless and wished to travel again.

So they fitted him out and sent him forth, and he went into wild places, where Hallmund told him it was safe to go. He found a small and narrow valley in Goatland-jokul; it was so fenced about by mountains that the sun scarcely ever came in there. The glaciers were steep and high on every hand, and Grettir found it hard work to cross them, but at the bottom he found a little stream, and hot-springs which served to keep the earth warm and the glaciers away. There was good grass down there in the little meadows, and such a multitude of fat sheep that they were beyond count.

Grettir made himself a hut and dwelt there; he killed for meat what sheep he needed, but every evening at dusk he heard a great whooping from further along the valley, and then the sheep all went to the sound of that voice. At last Grettir met the owner of the voice; he was a giant called Thorir, a half-troll, and a friend to Hallmund, and so with him Grettir became friends. Grettir named the valley Thorir's-vale, after him. He had daughters, and they were all glad to see Grettir, for few had ever come to that place. But though they treated him well Grettir found it lonely there at last, without the company of men, and he went out into the world again. When he went away he set up a stone upon a certain place, and bored a hole through it; any one who looked through that stone could see the entrance to Thorir's-vale, and thus Grettir meant to be able to come there again. He went back to Ball-jokul, meaning to live with Hallmund again, and it was two years since he had seen him.

Now Hallmund, and Thorir too, told Grettir that in earlier times there was scarce a mountain or valley or river of the land that had not had a spirit or troll living in it and ruling there, and some were kind to men

and some were not. But most had
died since the coming of Christianity,
and Hallmund said that he knew his
own death was not far off. In truth
Hallmund died while Grettir was living with Thorir, and here is the tale
of the manner of his death.

There had come a man to Ernewater Heath, Grim of Kropp, an outlaw. Grim found Grettir's hut and
dwelt there, catching fish as Grettir
had done. Now Hallmund was displeased that any one lived there in
Grettir's place, and meant to make
life troublesome for him.

One day Grim caught a hundred
fish, and he dressed them and hung
them in the sun; but the next morning
they were gone without a trace, for
Hallmund had taken them. Then Grim
went for fish again, and caught still

more, and hung them up to cure them for the winter, but once more Hallmund came and took them all away. Then when Grim had caught still more, three hundred fish in all, he watched through the night, to find out who took his fish, and to stop that stealing.

In the night he heard the footsteps of some heavy thing, and looking out through the chinks of the hut he saw a great man with a pannier on his back. The man came cautiously, but did not see Grim; he set down the basket and filled it with the fish; when they were all in, the load seemed big enough for a horse; but the man stooped down and shouldered the basket, and was about to go off with it. Then Grim rushed out and struck at him with an **axe,** and wounded him deeply in the neck. Hallmund leaped away, and ran thence at a great pace.

Grim followed after, and tracked him by the blood till he came to the cave. There he heard voices talking, and so he peered within, and listened. There by a fire sat Hallmund, and his daughter was trying to stanch the blood; but he told her that this was his death, and told also how it had happened. Then he sang of his deeds, bidding his daughter listen as he sang and cut the song in runes upon a staff. This she did, and Grim listened also, and got the song by heart. Hallmund sang:

"Hallmund am I,
Who here must die;
A friend to man
Long time I've been.

In manly play
I drew away
My bridle-bands
From Grettir's hands.

With Grettir stout,
In another bout,
We two fought them
'Gainst eighty men.

There in our plight
Grettir showed might,
And many fell
Before his skill.

Yet more lay low
Beneath my blow,
Until that hand
Fled from the land.

Oft have I through
The giant's crew
My weapons driven,
With trolls have striven,

Till mountain sprites
And evil wights
Now flee with dread
Before my tread."

And Hallmund told in his song all of his exploits, for he had lived long and had gone into all parts of the island.

His daughter said, "Who will now avenge thy death?"

"Grettir would avenge me if he were here," said Hallmund. "Yet he that slew me is a lucky man, and will come safely away."

Then he sang more of his song, but at last he died. Then Grim came out of his hiding and spoke to the daughter where she sat weeping, and said that he slew Hallmund in defending his own goods. She said the deed was not evil in such a case, and bade him go in peace. Grim lived on the heath that winter, but then he got ship and went away out of Iceland, and took to trading and became a great man.

When Grettir came back to Balljokul he found that Hallmund was dead, and Grim was safe away from venegance. Nothing more is known of Hallmund's daughter, nor of the giant Thorir.

CHAPTER X

GRETTIR AT SAND-HEAPS

NOW Grettir lived some years more
in the wastes, and seldom came
into settled parts, but at last the life
grew too wearisome to be borne. He
made up his mind to go more among
men, happen what might, and he
turned his back on the heaths and
never saw them again. But he went
away toward Isledale in Bard-dale,
where he had heard there might be
something for him to do for the good
of the land.

The farm of Sand-heaps had long
been troll-haunted, and of late years
the hauntings had grown worse. There
had lived at the farm a man named

Thorstein the White, with his wife Steinvor, and no harm had ever come to the folk of the place, though sometimes to the cattle. Now it had always been Steinvor's custom to go on the day before Christmas to the farm of Isledale-river, where her kinsmen dwelt, so that she could go to church on Christmas-eve.

Two years before she had gone away as usual, and her household that night had gone safely to bed. But in the night the noise of a struggle had been heard near the farmer's bed; no one dared to go there for fear of the sounds, but in the morning he was gone, and the woodwork broken, and the place marked as by a struggle. There was no trace of the farmer, nor had any since been found.

On the next Christmas the goodwife

went away to her kinsmen, and the
house was in the care of the house-
carle; but in the morning he had
vanished, and nothing was ever seen
of him. So now a third Christmas
was coming on, and no one knew what
might happen at the farm. But the
priest went there, and blessed the
house, and sprinkled it with holy
water, and exorcised all spirits that
might dwell in the hills or in the river,
so that there was some hope of seeing
no more of the trolls. Then the goodwife made ready to go home to her
people for Christmas-eve, and wished
to take with her her little daughter.
But this year the stream was very high,
for there was a great thaw, and the
river was swollen and full of ice, so
that the goodwife thought she must
stay at Sand-heaps.

On the day before Christmas there came to Sand-heaps a large man, very tattered, and rough of look; he asked the goodwife if he might stay there, and said his name was Guest. He was so huge and strong that the servants were afraid of him, but the mistress said he might stay there to eat and sleep, though she could not promise him safety.

"I will see to that," said he.

"Thou must be very brave," she said. "As for me, I would not spend Christmas here if I could get across the river."

"I will set thee across," he said. So she made ready to go, and they went as far as the river, she and her daughter and Guest; but when she saw the flood she cried out that neither man nor horse could get across safely, and so they must turn back.

"I can carry you both across," said Guest.

"Take the child first," said she. But he said he would not make two trips of it.

"Thou canst not carry us both," she said, and then her heart failed her and she wished to go back.

But Guest lifted her and set her on his shoulder, and picked up the child and put her in her mother's lap. Thus he had one arm free, and so he strode into the water, and the mother clung to her child, and they both were speechless from fear.

When he had come into deep water, there came a great cake of ice down the stream and drove hard against him. He could not avoid it, but he put out his arm and thrust the ice away from him. He went in deeper, until he was up to his shoulders, and more ice came against him, but always he warded it off. So he went on till the stream grew shallower, and then he came to shore. He put down the woman and the child, and she thanked him, and hurried on. By that time it was late, and she reached church just as folk were going in. They were astonished to see her and asked how she had come across the flood. She said she could not tell whether it was a man or a troll that had carried her.

The priest said it must have been a man, and a man of great might. "And if he sleeps at thy house to-night we may hear news in the morning." So they all went in to church, and she slept that night at the house of her kindred.

But Guest went back across the stream, and came to Sand-heaps, and ate his supper. Then he sent all the servants, men and women, to their sleeping-places, and he barred them in strongly, while they dared say nothing against it. He set a light there in the hall, and lay down upon a seat to wait what might happen, and stayed there till almost midnight.

Then he heard a great noise, and the outer door burst open, and into the hall came a great troll-woman, with a chopping-trough in one hand and a huge meat-chopper in the other. She looked about her as a woman might who came into her store-room to get meat, and saw Guest, and ran toward him. But he sprang up and caught hold of her, and she dropped the trough and chopper, and they began a great wrestling.

The troll-woman tried to bring him to the door; they struggled all about the place, and broke down the seats and benches, and smashed the wall-panelling, but she got him out to the door at last. Then she tried to drag him through the door, and could not for a long time, so hard did he resist; but finally she bore out not only Guest, but the very door frame on her shoulders. She cast aside the door frame, and tried to heave up Guest to carry him; but he clung to her waist, and twisted this way and that, and she could not lift him from the ground. All the time the men and women lay still in the house, and dared not make a sound.

Then the troll-woman tried to drag

Guest to the river, where it flowed not far from the farm. There was no ford there, but a great waterfall, and toward that she sought to bring him. Now he struggled mightily, and held back, and often sought to draw the sword that he had at his side, but she kept him too busy to do that, nor would he let her get the sword away from its place. So they wrestled back and forth, zig-zag across the plain, but ever she managed to get him by little and little nearer to the waterfall, and at last she brought him to the very edge, where the stream rushed down into a whirlpool.

They had fought so long that it was almost day, and Guest was terribly tired and almost without strength, but he saw that if she could cast him over the edge it would be the end of him. Not once had she let him get a hand free, but now he strove with great horror and anguish, and tore his right arm loose, and drew his sword, and hewed off her arm. Then her clutch of him was broken, and she fell backward into the river, and was carried down the waterfall. But Guest fell there without strength, and lay a long while upon the brink of the falls, and could not move for weariness.

But when it was broad day he roused himself and went to the farmhouse. By that time the folk had got out from their sleeping-places, by the breaks which Guest and the troll-woman had made in the panelling, and they were marvelling over the trough and chopper, and were thinking Guest was dead. He came in all bruised and sore.

Then the goodwife, Steinvor, came

home from church, for the flood had abated, and when she looked about her house she thought its fittings were well broken. Then she went to Guest and he told her all that had happened; and there were the chopper and the trough to prove the truth of it.

"But no common man art thou," she said. "What is thy true name?"

"My name is Grettir, Asmund's son," said he. Then she began to say much of the deed he had done, but he would not let her praise him, and said the affair was not yet finished; and he wished the priest might be sent for, for Grettir himself was too sore to travel. So the priest was sent for, and he came, and as soon as he set eyes on Grettir he knew what man he was.

"But," said the priest, "I will not

tell of thee. Yet now say what can have become of those men whom the troll-wife must have carried away, these past two Yules, and how can we find their bones to give them Christian burial?"

"The troll-wife must have carried them into the waterfall," said Grettir, "as she meant to do to me. It is my opinion that other trolls may dwell there still, and that is why I wished to see thee."

The priest could not be brought to believe that more trolls could be there, and so nothing was done about it at that time. Yet Grettir said he would not rest until he had made sure, as soon as his bruises would allow him to get about. The priest went back to his home, and Grettir lay in bed there for some days more.

But when he was well he went to the house of the priest, and asked him to come to see if there was not perhaps something to be seen by the waterfall. They went there and looked closely, and thought they saw that there was a cave behind the water; but they could not be certain, and could not get to the place because of the steepness of the rocks. Then Grettir drove a stake into the ground at the edge of the cliff, and let down a rope into the whirlpool at the bottom of the fall; the rope had a stone on its end to keep it in place.

"Surely thou wilt not go down," said the priest. "No man can do such a thing."

"It can be done if a man is strong enough to do it," answered Grettir. "Now I am going down, but do you stay here by the rope, to pull me up when I come out."

"Shall I let thee down?" asked the priest.

"It will do me no good against those whom I may find behind the water-fall, if I come there cumbered with a rope," answered Grettir.

Then he laid off all his outer clothes, and hung the short-sword at his belt, and so he dove into the waterfall. The last the priest saw was the soles of Grettir's feet; then he sat down to wait, and told his beads. But Grettir was carried down by the stream to the very bottom of the whirlpool; then he turned under the fall and swam that way, striving mightily against the eddy, until he came up under the waterfall and behind it. There was the mouth of a huge cave, and in front of it was a rock on which he climbed. There he stood for a while to get his breath, with the curtain of the waterfall behind him, and the black cave in front.

Then he drew his sword and went up into the cave, but when he had gone but a few steps, and looked around a corner of rock, there he saw a fire burning, and beside it was sitting a giant of great size and fierce countenance. When he saw Grettir he roared aloud, and leaping up, snatched up a bill and struck at him with it. It was a great bill on a wooden shaft, and the giant smote furiously; but Grettir hewed the shaft in two, and no harm came of the blow. Then the giant turned to reach for a sword that hung above his head, but Grettir rushed at him, and plunged his sword into the giant's side, and smote him to the death, so that he sprang aloft, and fell headlong, and rolled into the waterfall, and Grettir saw him no more.

But the priest, who sat above and watched, saw of a sudden that the waterfall was all bloody; and then the whirlpool was streaked with blood, and after that the river itself. So he was frightened, thinking that Grettir was dead, and wondering what next would happen to himself. Then he rose up and ran home. There he told how Grettir had come to his death, and mourned for the death of such a man.

In the cave Grettir took brands from the fire and explored the place, and there he found, men say, much gold that he stowed within his belt. He found, too, the bones of two men, and those men must have been the farmer of Sand-heaps and his house-carle. Grettir put the bones of the men into a bag, and when he had finished looking about him he leaped again into the waterfall, taking the bag with him. So he came down into the whirlpool, and came up outside the fall, and swam to the rope, and cried to the priest to haul him up. No answer could he get, and so he had to climb the rope; it was a long climb up the cliffs, and a hard one, for Grettir was weary. But he reached the top, and went with the bag of bones to the church at Isle-river, and left the bag in the porch. With it he left a staff, and on it he cut these rhymes:

"Into the stream's great fall I dove,
  And to the cave behind it strove,
  Where, though the river pressed me down,
  In spite of all its strength I won.

"There the cave-dweller leaped at me,
In hope to slay me speedily.
But in his breast I sheathed my sword
And won his wealth as my reward;
While now I lay on holy ground
The bones of men which there I found."

Then Grettir went back to Sand-heaps, and the priest found the bones in the porch in the morning. When next the priest met Grettir he made him tell all that had happened, but Grettir brought the priest to admit that he had not stayed by the rope, in manly fashion.

After that the bones were buried in the churchyard, and no more haunt-ings ever happened in the vale, so that Grettir was much praised for ridding the land of the trolls. But though Grettir stayed there through the winter, it was known who he was, because the priest had bewailed his death. So word of it got abroad, and came to Thorir of Garth. As soon as the spring opened he sent men for Grettir's head, but Grettir was warned, and he went away before they came.

Grettir at Sand-heaps 169

CHAPTER XI

GRETTIR AT FAIRWOOD-FELL

WHEN Grettir left Sand-heaps
he went over the hills to Holm,
where dwelt Biorn the Champion of
Hitdale, a famous and bold chief, who
often gave shelter to outlaws. His
ancestors and Grettir's had been friends
and he was friendly to Grettir. He
welcomed his guest well, and Grettir
asked if he might live there with him.

"That is not possible," said Biorn,
"for thy enemies are great, and are hot
against all who harbor thee. But I
can tell thee what thou canst do, if
thou carest for my word."

Grettir said that he did.

"Well," said Biorn, "here I live at feud with my neighbor Thord Kolbein's son, and his men harry my lands by stealth, and do me what evil they can. Now there is a place where thou canst abide, in the mountain overlooking all the plain and all the roads in these parts, so that thou canst take thy toll from all who go or come. It is no man's land, and I will not disturb thee there if thou wilt not prey on my men, but of what thou mayest do to Thord and his men I say nothing. And though thou mayest not live here with me, still we may be often together."

Grettir liked that advice, and he went to the stronghold which Biorn showed him. It was a cave between two slides of stones up which no man might walk, and one man might defend the path that ran up between the slides. From below one could look right through the mountain, but Grettir walled up the back with great stones, so that no one could get at him from that side, and the overhanging top would protect him. After that he hung gray cloth before the place, so that again it looked as if one could see through, and no one would know that a man dwelt there. The mountain was called Fairwood-Fell.

Then Grettir dwelt in that place, and lived the merriest life in many a long day. For he took what he wished from all such travellers as were not Biorn's men; but Biorn's men were all friendly to him, and he was often with them and with Biorn himself. In Biorn's saga it is said that he and Grettir were equal in strength, but men agree that Grettir was the strongest man that ever lived in Iceland, though many strong men had lived there before him. Grettir and Biorn did many feats together: once they swam the length of Hitriver, and at another time those two alone brought to the ford of the river the great stepping-stones that have been there ever since, for neither floods nor ice have moved them.

But Thord Kolbein's son found it hard that Grettir dwelt there and preyed on his men, since they lost much at his hands. For a long time no one knew for sure that it was Grettir, and then none knew where he dwelt, and when they learned they cared not to go against him in such a place. One day Grettir went down among Thord's farms, and at one place he took four fat rams and drove them away before him. The shepherds followed after, six of them, and tried to coax the sheep away from Grettir as he drove them before him; but the men dared not set on Grettir. Then the rams, knowing the shepherds, turned various ways, so that Grettir could not keep them together. In anger he caught two of the men and hurled them senseless on the ground; then he hooked the rams together by the horns, two and two, and threw a pair over each of his shoulders and so carried them away.

When this news was brought to Thord he was in talk with a man named Gisli, who had just landed from West-over-the-Sea. Gisli was a great trader and traveller, a large strong man, fond of fine clothes and something of a boaster; he listened to the tale which was told to Thord, and asked:

"If this fellow is but one man alone, why canst thou not get rid of him?"

"He has often been too much for many men," answered Thord, "and his stronghold would be hard to win. But I am angered all the time by him, since I know that my neighbor Biorn laughs while I suffer."

"Well," said Gisli, "I am sorry I cannot be here this winter, to rid thee of him."

"Art thou so sure thou couldst do it?" asked Thord.

"I have met worse than he, and vanquished them," said Gisli. "I have been with the greatest kings and men of war in my journeys, and no one has ever got the best of me. I should not be afraid to stand alone before him."

"If thou canst slay him thou wilt be well paid," said Thord. "Six marks of silver are offered for his head, but he who earns the money will have to work."

"I will earn it," said Gisli, greedy for the money. "Now tell me where is his lair, and whether, if I go by in sight of it, he will not come out against me. If I have but a couple of men with me he will not be afraid, and then we can slay him. I have long wished to meet with Grettir."

"Speak not so loud here," said Thord, "but come and I will tell thee what is best to do."

So they went and talked it over in secret, but their talk had been over-heard by one who brought it to Biorn, and he brought it to Grettir. "But," said Biorn, "if thou goest out to meet

Gisli, slay him not, for thou wouldst but add his family to thy foes. Yet a good drubbing would do no harm, and would take down his pride a bit."

Grettir smiled, but promised nothing.

Gisli stayed with Thord while his ship was being laid up for the winter, and while he was selling his goods in the neighborhood. When his business was finished he started for Burgfirth, and he led behind him two horses loaded with gifts for his kinsmen, and with his own clothes and money. He was well-armed, and so were two men who went with him; they were men of the neighborhood, whom he had hired to go with him past Grettir's lair.

"And," he said before setting out, "we will ride in bright holiday clothes, so that the outlaw shall not fail to see us, and come to see what we have."

So they rode on the journey, and came after a while to the heath below Grettir's stronghold. The men showed it to Gisli, and he said it was a hard place to get at, but he trusted the outlaw would come to meet them.

Grettir from his lair looked down and saw them, and saw that because they rode so few, and in such bright clothing, it was a challenge for him to come down to them. So he took up his weapons, and leaped on the slide, where the stones lay on such a steep slope that any weight would make them slip. Down he went sliding, stones and all, with a great noise, to put himself in Gisli's way.

"Here he comes," said Gisli, "running like a fool into the trap. Now off from your horses, and set upon him boldly when I bid you."

So they dismounted, and Grettir came up to them, and took hold of the bridle of one of the pack-horses. "I will take this horse and his load," said he, "for I need a few things for the winter."

"Dost thou know whom thou wouldst rob," said Gisli, very grandly.

"Thou seemest not a very great man," said Grettir. "But I am not fussy, and even if thy goods are cheap, I will not mind."

"But I will, then," said Gisli. "Set on him, men, and see that he does not escape."

Then the men drew their swords and attacked Grettir. He took his sword and shield and defended himself, but gave way before them to a rock that stood there upright by the roadside. Grettir himself had heaved the rock from the bed and stood it up, to show the way to travellers in winter, and it has ever since been called Grettir's Heave. There he defended himself for a while, with the stone at his back; and he saw how Gisli, while he made much noise and great pretense, kept always behind his men and out of danger. So Grettir grew tired after a few minutes of that game, and dealt one of the men such a blow that he laid him dead. Then he came out from his place and struck down the other man, so that he and Gisli were face to face.

"Now thou hast not thy men to defend thee," said Grettir, "so show what thou canst do."

"Thou art a fiend," said Gisli.

He struck very weakly, but Grettir smote so hard that presently Gisli threw away sword and shield and fled along the hillside. There was no place on the heath where he could go, but he ran as hard as he could, and Grettir followed after him, keeping a little distance between them. Gisli kept looking back, and whenever he seemed tired Grettir would close up the distance between them, and Gisli would run faster. So they kept on, and Grettir thought it great sport to keep Gisli so hard at work; they ran a long way, two leagues and more, and still Gisli ran as hard as he could. He cast off his outer clothing bit by bit, hoping that Grettir would stop for it, but Grettir still came on. Then Gisli dropped his belt and knife; they were very handsome, but Grettir let them lie, and followed on. Gisli after that cast down his purse, but it stopped Grettir no more than the other things, and he gave Gisli no rest. At last Gisli had no more clothing than his shirt and breeches, and was getting very tired, so Grettir as he ran pulled up a bush, and made its twigs into a bunch. Then they came to a river, and Gisli ran to it, thinking he would rather drown there than fall into Grettir's hands. Now the river was full of ice, and Grettir did not care to swim, so he put on speed and ran in on Gisli, and caught him. From labor and fear Gisli had scarcely strength to struggle, and Grettir quickly pressed him to his knees.

"Art thou the man," he asked, "that wished to meet with Grettir?"

"Keep my goods," said Gisli, "but let me go."

"Here is something for thee first," said Grettir.

Then he pulled up Gisli's shirt and flogged him with the switches till Gisli roared like any boy. So then Grettir laughed and let him go. Gisli went to the nearest house and lay in bed a week before he could travel, because he was so stiff and sore; but Grettir went back along the way he had come, and took up what he wanted of Gisli's belongings, and brought them to his lair. There he lived for a second winter, and no one came against him.

When the next summer was nearly finished, then Grettir set out to get provision for the winter, and here and there he got together things from travellers and farmers, and because the farmers had what he wanted, he took the most from them. Now they were all Thord's men, and they complained to Thord, saying that this was **not to** be borne longer, and bidding him to clear the country of such a pest. So Thord sent out word to the neighbors that they should make ready to set on Grettir when next he should come out. His own house-carles should go also, and his son at their head.

It was not long before Grettir came out again for meat; this time he had two men with him, they were from Biorn's farms. Grettir went among Thord's farms, and here he took sheep and there he took cattle, till he had a goodly lot together, and then made ready to return with them. But word had been sent round at his first coming, and now the country-side had been roused against him. As he and his men went back along Hitriver, driving the beasts before them, they

saw men coming up behind them, one
band nearer and the other farther off;
and across the river was still another
band, hurrying to reach a ford.

Grettir and his men could have got
away had they left the beasts, but
Grettir never would give up what once
he had laid his hand on. So now he
drove the sheep and cattle upon a
point of land that ran out into the
river. The neck of the point was
narrow, and there Grettir made ready
to defend himself, with his men at his
back. "So long as ye let none get
behind me," said he, "I can keep
them off."

Then the first band came up, and
set on him gingerly, being somewhat
afraid of him. Their leader was an
old man, and he egged on his men but
did not fight himself. Grettir smote

among them briskly, and slew some and wounded others, so that they drew off and watched him till the second band came up. These said they would go in and see what they could do; their leaders were young men, Thrand and Thorgils, Finnbogi and Steinulf, men of property, and the whole band set on hotly.

This was a brisk fight, and the men across the river came to the ford and were now crossing it, so that they would join in the fight before long. Grettir defended himself for a while, till he had some wounds, and both the men behind him were hurt. Then he thought that he must die there, and wished that some men of note should fall there with him. Caring no longer what defense he had at his back, he sallied out into the band that stood before him. First with his short-sword he struck Steinulf, and cleft him to the breast-bone; then he slashed Thorgils in the waist, and almost cut him in two. Thrand rushed at him to avenge his kinsmen, but Grettir with a back-hand blow took all the flesh from the outside of his thigh, so that Thrand fell and could not get up again. After that Grettir cut his way through the band to Finnbogi, and thrust him in the breast.

Then the old man, the leader of the first band, who had stood watching, called on the fighters to leave Grettir, for they could do nothing against him, while he chose his prey at will. So they fell back and left Grettir there. The third band was very slow in passing the river, so now Grettir and his two men began again to drive the beasts away, while the men of the place stood at a distance and bound up their wounds. Almost every one of them was hurt, and they had no more spirit against him.

When the third band at last came up, and saw what wounds Grettir had given, and how many he had slain, they were in no haste to follow him, so he got clear away with his booty. The leader of that band was ill thought of after that; he was Arnor the son of Thord.

The place where they fought is still called Grettir's Point. Men of note had fallen there, and the folk of the valleys were much stirred up about it. Some of the slain had been kin to Biorn of Hitdale, Grettir's friend; and now many came to him, and bade him chase Grettir away. Biorn said Grettir should not stay there longer than that winter, and so he told Grettir when those two met.

"It is plain," said Biorn, "that the country is very hot against thee, and I shall have heavy feuds on my hands because of thee; besides, thou hast slain both kin and friends of mine, and it will not be to my honor to let thee stay here after this winter."

Grettir said that he had slain but to defend his own life, and if he must go forth he knew not where to go, for many quarters of the country were now closed to him, because he was known there and men would hunt him for the reward.

But Thord, when he knew that Grettir would stay until the spring, sent to Thorir of Garth, and told where Grettir was, and how he might be taken. The winter closed in hard, and Thorir could do nothing then, but as soon as the roads could be used in the spring he started out with all his band, and crossed the hills. He lodged himself at Thord's house, and went out upon the mountain one morning in the fog, with Thord to bring him to Grettir's lair.

That morning Grettir was also abroad, and had one man with him. There was a stone hut there on the mountain side, with steps leading up to it; it was a shelter for shepherds, and Grettir and his man, on their horses, were by the hut when the fog began to lift and they saw before them, coming up the mountain, Thorir and all his band, who would see them soon.

Grettir and his man could not hide

behind the hut, for the horses would be seen; and where horses were on that hillside there must also be men. So Grettir leaped from his horse, and took it in his arms, and carried it up the steps into the hut; then he carried in his man's horse, and they stayed in the hut, and watched to know if they had been seen.

But Thorir and his men went on, over a shoulder of the mountain, to reach Grettir's lair.

"Now," said Grettir, "it would be a pity if they did not meet me after coming so far; and besides, I have no wish that they rummage my house. So I will go to meet them."

His comrade could not dissuade him. Grettir put on a cloak that he took from his saddle, and a slouched hat; he went by a by-path till he came before Thorir's band. Then he came into their sight, bent like an old man, and leaning on a staff. Thorir rode up to him and asked him if he had seen Grettir that morning. Thord was there close by.

"That I have," said Grettir, "and you have just missed him. He was eating his meal just beyond that mountain tarn, and you can ride straight over yon hummocky ground and catch him behind the rock on that hillside."

So Thorir and his men rode hastily the way he pointed, onto the rough ground, where there were hummocks and tufts of marsh grass. Grettir got out of sight and watched them, and saw them ride straight into a bog, as he had wished. There they floundered for the rest of the day, and cursed heartily the old shepherd who sent them there.

Grettir, as soon as he saw them well bemired, went back to his man. They took their horses and rode away, and came to the house of Thord, where his daughter in fine attire stood out of doors and watched them come. Then Grettir rode up to her and sang this song:

> "Tell to Thord when he comes home,
> I was here while he did roam.
> And bid Thorir truly say
> Who was in the bog to-day.
> Tell to both — it is no lie —
> Grettir leaves them a good-by."

She got those lines by heart and told them to Thord and Thorir when they came back. Then they knew that Grettir meant to leave those valleys, and Thord was glad of it. But when Thorir knew he had had his journey for his pains, and had been so fooled, then he was very angry, and he set a greater price on Grettir's head, making it nine marks of silver.

But Grettir rode to Biorn's house, and said good-by, and thanked Biorn for all his friendship, and rode away out of those parts, in which he was never seen again. He rode northwest, and lived on the land during the summer, now here and now there, seizing what he needed, but never finding a friend who dared to give him shelter. For it was known everywhere how Thorir had set a larger price on his head, and would call before the courts any one who would harbor Grettir. So men were both afraid to befriend him and tempted by the reward for him. Even his relatives dared not keep him under their roofs, and wherever he stayed for a while, though it were on a barren hill-top, men were sure to learn of him and likely to gather together to take him.

And now his life grew very dreary, and he was burdened by his troubles, for his dread of the dark grew on him more and more, and he was very lonely. By now he had been sixteen winters in outlawry, and that was longer than any outlaw had ever lived in Iceland, for Gisli the Soursop had lived longer than all others before Grettir, and he was slain in his fourteenth year. Now Grettir began to wonder if he should be slain like Gisli, nor did he care very much if that should happen. Twenty Winters must be passed in outlawry before he could be released and spoken free of his guilt, and four years more seemed a long time.

CHAPTER XII

GRETTIR GOES TO DRANGEY

SNORRI the Priest, already named in the story, one day grew angry with his son Thorod for something that he had done; his fault is not told, but it is plain that Snorri thought that Thorod lacked manliness. For Snorri sent the young man away from his house, bidding him not return till he had killed some outlaw, or done some feat.

Thorod went about until he heard where there was an outlaw on a farm among the Broadfirth dales. He went thither and found the farmer's wife at home, and asked her where that outlaw might be.

She asked, "What do you want of him?"

"To slay him," said Thorod.

"Why," she said, "he is but a lad, and he is not outlawed throughout the land, but only if he goes away from this place. He has not gone away, so he is safe from thee; but I can tell thee a deed to do."

"What is that?" asked Thorod.

"Among these hills lurks Grettir the Strong," said she, "and he has already taken much from the farmers. It is more to thine honor if thou slayest him."

The young man said to himself that he would win his honor back even if he fell before Grettir, so he hunted until he found him. Grettir was lolling in a sunny place, with his horse tied near, and his arms at hand. Thorod told his name, and said: "I have an errand in these parts. Shall I tell it to thee?"

"I care not what men's errands are," said Grettir, "but only what they have. Still, since thou art the son of Snorri thou mayest go free of me."

"But I have come to fight thee," said Thorod.

"That is marvellous," said Grettir, amused. "Has no one told thee that there is little good fortune to be pried out of me?"

"I know that, and there is no help for it," said Thorod. "I must slay thee or thou me." And he drew his sword.

When Grettir saw he was in earnest he rose up and defended himself with his shield, but he did not draw his sword. Thorod struck with all his might, but he could not pass Grettir's

Defended Himself with His Shield

guard. Then Grettir said, "This will not help thee nor hurt me. Leave off now."

Yet Thorod still struck furiously, willing to die there if only he might accomplish something. When Grettir saw he was not to be persuaded, he put aside the blow with great force, and strode in on Thorod, and picked him up, and set him down on the ground. Grettir sat down beside him and held him, and Thorod could do nothing more. Said Grettir:

"Now it is time for thee to stop, and if thou hadst been any one else I would have slain thee before now. I have no fear of thee; but I do fear thy father, the old graybeard whose wisdom is too much for most men. So go away now, and try for something more within thy power."

Thorod saw he could do nothing, and so he rode away, and went home, and told his father what he had done. Snorri said:

"Grettir was right, for had he slain thee I must have avenged thee; but now I will help him all I can, with my counsels. As for thee, though foolhardy, thou hast shown courage, and I will take thee back again."

After Grettir had sent Thorod away, he remembered that Snorri the Priest had once been his friend, and might help him again; so he also went to Tongue, and came to Snorri's hall, and asked him for help.

"For my dread of the dark has so increased," said Grettir, "and such horrible shapes appear before me all the night long whenever I am by myself, that I can scarcely bear it longer, and must soon have a companion, even though he betray me to my death. May I live here with thee?"

"It would not be right for me, a priest of the law," said Snorri, "to harbor thee, an outlawed man. Nor would it help thee much, for many men come and go, and all have heard of the price on thy head, and news would soon be brought to Thorir of Garth. But thou shouldst go to some place where thou needest not venture forth for food, and yet may defend thyself against whoever may come."

"I know not of any such place," said Grettir.

"Go thou," said Snorri, "to the island of Drangey, which lies in Skagafirth, a league from shore. One man alone can defend it, for it is all one cliff; there are ladders in one place, and if the uppermost is pulled up, no one can molest thee."

"How can I get out there?" asked Grettir.

"That thou must find out for thyself."

"Well," Grettir said, "I will see what I can do. But I will not dwell there alone."

"Then be sure of thy comrade," said Snorri. "And it is hard to see into a man's heart."

Then Grettir went away, thanking Snorri for his counsel, and journeyed once more into his own country, and came to his mother's house. There his mother and his brother gave him food, and he slept out of doors in various places; for while it was summer he was not haunted so much, and it was the winter that he dreaded the most. His brother Illugi was now a well-grown lad of fifteen winters, and a great help to his mother.

One day his mother asked Grettir what he would do for the winter, for it was not to be hoped that he could stay there where he was. Grettir said: "To Drangey will I go if by any means I can get out there, and there I will stay till my outlawry is over. But I will not live there alone, and yet I know not who will go with me."

Illugi heard this. He was a handsome lad and the joy of his mother. It was foretold of him that he would grow into a goodly man, and the luckiest of his family, if once he could come into his manhood. Now Illugi said:

"Take me with thee, Grettir. No great help can I be to thee, but I will always give thee a brother's aid so long as I may."

"Gladly will I take thee," said Grettir, "if only our mother can spare thee."

"Here is a hard choice between my needs and thine," said Asdis, their mother. "But if once thou canst get out from thine outlawry, Grettir, then I know that thine ill luck will fall away from thee, and the greatness of our family will begin. As thy need is so great, I give Illugi to thee, yet it is a hard thing to see both of you go from me." With that she gave way to tears; but she kept to her word, and made them ready for the journey, with clothes and food and what money she could spare.

When they were fitted out they lingered yet a few days, till winter set in and Grettir's hauntings grew worse again, so that he could no longer sleep alone out of doors. So they set out for Drangey, and Asdis set them on their road. But when they parted she said:

"Now ye go away from me, O my sons, and never shall I see you again. Bad have been my dreams, and I forebode evil of this journey; neither of you shall come back to me. In Drangey shall ye be smitten with the sword, and there shall ye be buried, for so my fears tell me. Yet for hope that ye may yet escape, remember to stand by each other manfully. Keep yourselves from all wiles, and most of all beware of witches, for they are still here and there in the land."

"We will meet our fate, whatever it may be," said Grettir. "And if

our foes come against us, thou shalt
not need to feel shame for the courage
of thy sons."

And there they left her, weeping.

Then they went north and visited
their kindred as they went, but kept
on their journey till they came near
Skagafirth. Then as they journeyed
late in the day they passed by Dinby;
the weather was very bitter, but Grettir
went unhooded, for so he went in all
weathers. When they had passed the
place a man came after and caught up
with them, a lean and shambling fellow, with a big voice and a foolish
face. Grettir and Illugi said nothing
to him, but he came and joined them,
and talked. He said his name was
Thorbiorn, and his nickname Noise;
and a noisy no-account fellow he was,
but Grettir was glad to joke with such

a one, who knew all the gossip of the country-side, and could sing a jolly song.

"They stared at thee at Dinby," said Noise, "and wondered if thou wouldst dread men as little as the cold, for none of them were willing to go out in such weather, strong men as they were."

"I saw two of them as I went past," said Grettir, "and I should not be afraid of them, at any rate."

"If thou art such a man," said Noise, "I should like to go with thee and serve thee."

Grettir would neither take him on nor turn him away, for his talk was good sport, and so Noise followed them until they got used to him. Then they came to Skagafirth, and saw how, a league from shore, there stood up a huge cliff out of the sea, steep and sheer on every side, and very tall.

"What place is that?" asked Grettir.

"That is Drangey," said Noise. "It is owned in shares by the Skagafirthers, who keep their sheep there."

"There are sheep there now?" asked Grettir.

"Many of them," said Noise, "and they are there the year round."

"There should also be birds on the cliffs," said Grettir.

"Aye, birds in plenty," answered Noise, "and good fishing too in places, if but the lines are long enough, so that men could live on the island and never come ashore."

"But do men live there?" asked Grettir.

"There is a house for shelter,"

answered Noise. "The farmers dwell there when they come for their sheep every autumn and spring. But no one lives there."

"Now," said Grettir, "I will go out to Drangey and live there with my brother, and thou mayest come if thou wilt; but good and faithful service will I require of thee."

Noise thought twice about that, for the company would be small; but he knew not where he should dwell that winter, since most folk in those parts were tired of him, and so he said he would go with Grettir. Then they went down to the farm at Reeks, where the goodman was named Thorwald. Grettir asked to be set over to Drangey in the farmer's boat; the man refused at first, but when Grettir gave him money he consented. He was a good friend to Grettir from that time forth.

Then the farmer launched his boat, and took Grettir and Illugi and their goods, and Noise, and rowed them over to the island that night by the light of the moon, so that no one should know who had set them over. When they came to the island the crags stood beetling up from the water, and Grettir did not see how they were to get upon the top. But in one place they found a little beach, and it was heaped with driftwood; from that place they got all their firewood so long as they lived on the island. And from the beach ladders led to the top of the cliffs, three ladders in all. The two lower ladders were fast to the rocks, strongly made of wood. But the uppermost was a rope-ladder, which dangled free, and when it was drawn up no one could reach the top. Grettir and those two landed, and thanked the farmer, and he rowed away home.

They climbed the ladders, and brought up their bundles, and took them to the house. It was a stone hut with a thatched roof; it had a fireplace and sleeping niches, but of room inside there was not overmuch. When it was day they looked about the island-top; there were plenty of sheep and rams, and they were all fat, for the pasture was good.

So Grettir, and Illugi his brother, and their man Noise, settled there on the island for the winter, which was the seventeenth winter of Grettir's outlawry.

On toward Christmas time, when meat was wanted for feasts, on a calm day those who owned sheep on Drangey sent boats out to the isle, to get sheep to bring home. When the sheep-owners came near the island, they saw there were men on the top, but guessed they must have come there by shipwreck. "They will be glad of our coming," thought the owners of the sheep. But when they came still nearer the men pulled up the rope-ladder, and at that the sheep-owners were amazed. They called up to know what that meant.

Grettir stood on the cliff's edge, and answered: "I am Grettir the Outlaw, and here have I made my home." Then they thought they had come into great difficulties. "Who brought thee here?" they asked.

"One who loved me better than he did you," said Grettir.

"Well," said the Skagafirthers, "we will put thee ashore again, and will never count up against thee the sheep thou mayest have killed."

"That is very kind," said Grettir, "but things must stand as they are. I have the island and I mean to keep it, and all that is on it. Get me away if you can, but I will not go while I live."

Then in one of the boats sprang up a man named Thorbiorn Angle, a rough and headstrong man, not loved, but very masterful; he and his brother owned nearly half the island. He was one-eyed and black-haired, a large strong man.

"I will get thee away," he shouted, "and if thou comest dead, then it will be the better for all Iceland."

But though he said that and more,

making threats of all kinds, in the end all the Skagafirthers had to row back home, and nothing that they could do would get Grettir from his stronghold. There he lived that winter, and a summer, and another winter, and had plenty of food of all kinds, for sometimes Thorwald of Reeks would row out secretly with flour, and sell it to Grettir for the money that he had. And they were well satisfied, though sometimes Noise had hard work to bring the driftwood up the ladders.

Now Noise was lazy and shiftless, and would loll about when he should be working, and sleep when he should be watching; for it was his duty to keep the fire going in the night, because, should their fire go out, they had no means of making more. One night when he slept, the fire went out.

When that was found in the morning Grettir was very angry, and threatened Noise with a thrashing; the man grumbled much, and said that his life was hard if he must remember everything. Then Grettir asked Illugi how they should get fire, for they must have it for their cooking, and though it was spring, the nights were still cold. Illugi said that they must wait till a ship came that way.

"Then we might wait forever," said Grettir. "And I see nothing else except for me to swim to shore."

"A league is a long way," said Illugi, in alarm. "And if thou art drowned, then we also are lost."

"Well, I must try it," said Grettir. So he stripped himself to his underclothes, and tied upon his head a cloak which he rolled up, so that he could wear it when he came to land. He had waited until night, that no one should see him swimming, and in the darkness he set forth. It was a long swim, but the night was calm, and he came safely to shore. Then he cast himself down for weariness, wrapped in his cloak, and slept until it was late in the day.

Then he roused himself and went up near the dwellings. There he found that it was Thing-day, and all the folk of the Heron-ness Thing were there about their lawsuits and their business. Then Grettir, for the love of seeing folk together, went to the Thing-place, and sat down on the outskirts of the crowd, with the hood of his cloak pulled over his head. He crouched together, and said nothing to any one, and watched from within his hood.

By that time the business of the Thing was done, and men had begun to think of sport, and to say that now the young men should wrestle. So now Thorbiorn Angle made himself very active, pushing and pulling folk about to form a ring, in which the men should strive. Then the weaker and younger wrestled first, and after that the older and stronger, till it was time for the very best of them to step forth.

Two men, brothers, both named Thord, were the strongest of all in that region. It was said that they had each of them the strength of two men, and when they wrestled neither could get the better of the other; but they were quiet and peace-loving. Now they were called upon to wrestle, and so they went about the ring, asking who would wrestle with them; but each man hung back, though all called on some one else to step forward. Then Thorbiorn Angle, looking about to see who might give them sport, saw where Grettir sat apart, and went to him, and pulled at him to drag him to the ring. But Grettir sat like a rock.

"Who art thou?" asked Thorbiorn. "No one else has ever sat so stock-still before me."

"My name is Guest," said Grettir from his hood.

"Wilt thou wrestle?" asked Thorbiorn. "A welcome guest wouldst thou be."

"It is a long time since I have wrestled," said he, "and here I am a stranger among you all. What if I should hurt a man?"

They all spoke and said that no one would blame him for that.

"Well," said he, "promise me the peace of your Thing, so long as I stay among you."

They all cried that that should be done, and one who cried the loudest of all was called on to speak the oath of peace. His name was Hafr, and he stood forth and spoke these words:

"Now do I proclaim peace among us, between all dwellers round about Skagafirth and this stranger here, until such time as he shall depart to his home. We promise him full peace and safety, whatever he may do among us, and full freedom henceforth from any deeds done here. Shame be upon him who breaks this peace! He shall be cast out from among us as far as wolves wander, Christians worship, or heathen sacrifice; as far as fires are built, as earth bears fruit, as children lisp their mother's name, or as the snow falls, or as men go on snowshoes, as fir-trees grow, as a falcon soars in spring, as the heavens stretch, as waters run, or as the winds blow. Let that peacebreaker be cast out from all homes. But here we shall be at peace, nor hold ill-will, as witness all who hear my words."

Then they all agreed, and they said that had been spoken well. The stranger stood up and said:

"Good is thy spoken word. Let me see if thy deeds are as fair."

And with that he threw off his cloak. Then all stared at him and fell back, for he was so huge that they knew him for Grettir himself. They broke up into groups and began to whisper among themselves, and Hafr felt himself a fool. Thorbiorn Angle began to go busily from group to group, to urge that they fall upon Grettir. "Great is the reward for him," he said, "and now we have him here without weapons or any defence." They all looked at Grettir askance, and he knew what they were thinking.

"Tell me what ye mean to do," said he. "Or how long will ye keep me waiting here without my cloak? It is all the same to me for your honor is concerned in it, and not mine." And he sang this song;

"Shall it be said in Skagafirth,
  Ye are men of little worth?
  Promise made is quickly broken;
  Soon shall all men see the token."

At that the leaders cried out that it should never be said of them that they broke their promised peace. Thorbiorn Angle looked black and went aside; but the wrestling ring was formed again, and the Thords were bidden to go against Grettir.

So first one of them went against him, and soon got a fall. And then the other was served the same. But after that they both wrestled against him, and that was a great sight, for neither could they get the better of him, nor he of them; he always had one of them beneath him, but the mastery was given to neither side. All three of them were much praised.

When the wrestling was finished, then some talk was made about Drangey; they asked him to give it up, but he refused. At dark he slipped away, and they knew not where he had gone; but Thorwald of Reeks gave him fire, and put him on the island as before, and there he lived yet another winter.

Then the owners of the island began to despair about their land and their sheep, and to the small holders it seemed very hard thus to lose all good from their property. They offered to sell their land and sheep to the richer holders, but none of them would consider the matter except Thorbiorn Angle. He offered small prices, and bought up all the other holdings, till he alone owned both the island and the sheep on it.

At the Althing that summer Grettir's relatives brought up the matter of his outlawry; he had been an outlaw twenty summers, and they asked that he be put back into the law again. Many of those who had suffered at his hands complained, saying that his deeds since he had been made an outlaw should be enough to keep him in outlawry; but the Lawman said that no outlaw's deeds should count against him in such a manner. Then they were about to set Grettir out of his outlawry.

But Thorir of Garth came before the courts, and bade the judges reckon again. Twenty summers indeed had Grettir been in outlawry, but only nineteen winters, so he must remain an outlaw one winter more. That was seen to be good law, and so the matter was dropped, except that it was known that in the next summer Grettir should be freed.

When Thorbiorn Angle heard that, he swore a great oath that before the next Althing he would have the island to himself, and gain the great reward by slaying Grettir.

CHAPTER XIII

OF THORBIORN ANGLE

UPON an autumn day Thorbiorn Angle launched his boat and told his men to row him out to Drangey. Grettir came to the cliff and talked with him, and Thorbiorn asked him once more to leave the island. Grettir said that he would not.

Said Thorbiorn: "If thou wilt go away I will pay thee well, for I have bought all the shares in the island, and it is mine now."

"If it is thine," said Grettir, "I will stay all the more gladly. I was sorry to deny the small holders, but thou art such a spiteful fellow that I am willing to spite thee a little."

"I will finish this and thee," said Thorbiorn.

"Do thy worst," said Grettir. Then Thorbiorn rowed away home, and wondered what he should do.

It was not long before a ship landed in Skagafirth, and one of those who came ashore was named Haering, a man so supple that it was said of him that he could climb any cliff. Thorbiorn Angle took him into his house; he told Haering that there were cliffs on Drangey that even he could not climb. Haering was young and very boastful; he began to urge Thorbiorn to take him out to see those cliffs, and said that he could do much service against Grettir. So they struck a bargain, and Thorbiorn agreed to pay Haering well if he slew Grettir.

Then one day they rowed out into

the firth, and came to Drangey on the cliff side, and there Thorbiorn set Haering upon the cliff, for upon that side the brothers kept no watch. Then Thorbiorn rowed around to the ladders, and Grettir came to the cliff, and spoke with him. Thorbiorn made great talk, and offered and promised many things, and begged Grettir to name some bargain to which he would agree. Grettir said he would agree to nothing, and bade Thorbiorn go away; but still he stayed, and held the two brothers in talk.

In the meantime Haering climbed the cliffs, which had never been done before. He ran across the island-top, and drew near the brothers where they stood talking with Thorbiorn. Haering had with him a little hand-axe, and he stole nearer Grettir and

Illugi, meaning to slay Grettir from behind. He began already to count his reward and to think upon his fame.

But then Grettir said to Illugi: "Why does this fellow in the boat hold us here in talk? Look behind, and say what thou seest."

Illugi looked, and said: "Here is a man close at hand, armed with an axe, and stealing up on us."

"Go against him," said Grettir, "and show me what thou canst do."

But when Haering saw Illugi turn upon him, drawing his sword, then his heart failed him, and he fled. Noise was at the hut, and Haering dared not flee there, and there was no other shelter on the island. Illugi chased him till he came to the cliff, and there

Haering leaped off, and was dashed to his death on the rocks, and that place is still named for him.

Illugi went back and told Grettir, and Grettir told Thorbiorn. "Thy man climbed well," said he, "but he had no heart in him."

Then Thorbiorn, cursing, turned his boat and went home, vowing that he would not come again without good reason.

Thorbiorn had a foster-mother, who now was all but bedridden by age, and an evil old crone she was. It was said of her that she had been a sorceress, but since the land had become Christian all heathen doings were forbidden by law, on pain of the lesser outlawry. When Thorbiorn came back from Drangey, and without either Grettir or Haering, he went to his foster-mother and complained bitterly of his fortune.

"Now," said he, "thou wast once a cunning woman. Canst thou not help me here, for all force is vain?"

"The old shoe is remembered when the new one pinches," said the old woman. "I can help thee, but thou must do as I say."

Thorbiorn promised that. "Then," said she, "on the next fair day shalt thou row out to Drangey again, and take me with thee in the boat. Men say that Grettir's luck will turn to good when once he comes out of his outlawry, and against a lucky man I can do nothing. But let me hear how he speaks with thee, and what he says to thy offers, and I can tell if his evil luck still follows him. If it does, I will bring him low before thee."

"Thou dost not promise me anything for my journey," said Thorbiorn, "and often enough have I been put to shame by going thither."

"Choose for thyself," said she.   "Go oftener, and get him; or go no more, and swallow all thy boasts."

So Thorbiorn went again, taking her with him in a boat with rowers; she lay down in the stern, and covered herself over with sailcloth. When they reached Drangey Grettir came to the edge of the cliff, to see who had come. Now Thorbiorn spoke fairly to Grettir, and made the best offers he had yet made, but still Grettir would not yield up the island.

Then the carline put her head out of the heap of cloth, and said: "Brave art thou, Grettir, but unlucky, and that thou showest by refusing the good that is offered thee. Now I see that thine end is at hand, and that we shall overcome thee."

Grettir started back, shuddering; never before had his soul so quailed within him as at the voice and the words of the old crone. "What devil is that?' asked he.

"Some woman is there in the stern," said Illugi.

"Rather a witch, of which our mother bade us beware," answered Grettir. "But she shall not have everything her own way against us."

Then he caught up a stone and hurled it at the boat; a marvellous long throw it was. Thorbiorn had thought them safe from all missiles, but the stone fell on the heap of cloth, and broke the leg of the old woman. She shrieked curses upon Grettir.

"I am sorry thou didst that," said Illugi. "Listen to her!"

"I wish the stone had found her head," answered Grettir. "Her curses are nought, for they come from her anger; but her prophecy was evil, since she read the fates."

Thorbiorn turned the boat about in all haste, and bade his men row home quickly. "This has been an unlucky journey," he said to his foster-mother, "and I shall have great shame from it."

"Yet I will overcome Grettir in the end," said she, "if only I recover from this hurt."

Thorbiorn wondered at the old woman's courage, but he did not believe her prophecy; he was much laughed at by his neighbors on account of this journey, and avoided going among men until they should forget it.

But the old woman's leg healed, until in a month she was able to hobble. By that time winter was drawing on, and one day she said to Thorbiorn; "Come with me down to the shore."

"No more of thy fooleries," he said. "They have given me trouble enough."

"No one will know of it save thee and me," said she. "Take thine axe and come."

So he took his axe and went with her to the shore, and there the old woman went straight to a certain spot as if she knew what she should find. There was lying a tree-trunk, as big as a man could carry; she looked it over, and nodded to herself. "Turn it over," said she.

Thorbiorn turned it over, and on the under side it had been both chafed and scorched. "Hew me," said she, "a flat place there where it has been marred."

So Thorbiorn hewed with his axe a flat place on the log. Then the old woman took a knife, and cut runes upon the log, and cut herself and marked the runes with her blood. Then she said charms and spells over them, bowing and muttering; and again she went around the log against the sun, walking backward and mumbling her charms. And after that she said to Thorbiorn:

"Now cast the log into the sea!"

So he took it and brought it to the water and pushed it out. The crone stood on the shore and said:

"To the isle, to the isle,
And do not fail!"

And then, though the wind and the

waves were toward the shore, the log floated out against them, and gathered way, and went with great swiftness, butting through the waves, going out toward Drangey. Thorbiorn stood and watched it until it was out of sight, and his mouth opened from amazement.

"Now," asked she, "wilt thou do what next I tell thee?"

"That I will, surely," said he.

Then they went back to Thorbiorn's house. But the log drove out to Drangey against the wind, and went ashore on the beach; in the morning when Grettir and Illugi came down the ladders they saw it lying there.

"Here is good firewood for us," said Illugi.

But Grettir looked at the log, and saw the runes, and shook his head. "This is some evil thing," he said,

"and my mind misgives me about it."
He cast it back into the sea, but on the
next morning it was there again, at the
foot of the ladders. "See," he said,
"how it has returned against the wind.
Now, though it comes back again, it
must not be carried up the ladders."
He cast it to sea again, with a mighty
heave, so that the landward-going
waves should take it, and he told Noise
of it, warning him never to touch it.
On the morrow it was on the beach
again, but they left it there.

Then the breeze that had been blow-
ing all these days turned into a gale,
with much rain. Grettir and Illugi
stayed in the house, and sent Noise for
firewood, and at first he brought all
else he could find, but left the log, as
he was bidden. Then they sent him
out late in the second day, and bade

him bring what else might have come to shore.

Noise went down the ladders, and found nothing more, but the log lay there still. Then he was angry with Grettir, and said to himself there was no harm in the log, and so brought it up the ladders, and carried it to the hut, and cast it down before the door, and called to Grettir to come out. Grettir came out with an axe. Now the dusk was falling.

"There is thy wood," said Noise. "Let me see thee be as quick in splitting it as I was in bringing it."

Grettir took no notice of the log, for Noise had turned the runes downward. but he struck at it with force, being angry with the man. But scarcely had the axe touched the wood when it glanced off sideways and into Grettir's leg, and sank into the bone above the knee. Grettir pulled it out, and looked at the log, and saw what Noise had done.

"Now," said Grettir, "evil has come home to us, and thou, Noise, hast disobeyed me. No man has ever given me such a wound as this, and I dread the outcome of it. If but once again thou forgettest to obey me, it will be thy death, and ours also."

CHAPTER XIV

THE DEATH OF GRETTIR

NOW that wound bled little. Illugi bound it up, and there was no pain to it; each day they dressed it, and by the third day the wound had grown together, while at night Grettir slept well. Illugi said the cut was healing.

"Then my forebodings are all false," said Grettir.

So he began the fourth night, and for a while slept well, but at last he waked and began to toss about. Illugi waked and asked if his leg pained him, and Grettir said that so it was. Then Illugi made a light and looked at the wound; it was red and angry, and the leg was swelling both above and below the wound.

"This is from that witch," said Grettir. "And now we must guard ourselves against what yet may come from her." Then he called Noise. "Do thou watch the ladders carefully, and whenever thou goest down for wood, pull up the last one when thou comest again."

Noise promised to do that. Then that next day the storm grew worse, with great cold, but each morning the brothers sent Noise out for firewood, and he went unwillingly. Then day by day Grettir's leg grew worse; it swelled from the ankle to the hip, and the wound itself festered exceedingly; Grettir was in great fever, and had no sleep because of his pain. Ten days he grew worse and worse, till Illugi looked for him to die.

On the eleventh day Grettir said to Noise: "Go out again for wood, and always be thou sure of the ladders."

Then said Noise in great heat: "What dost thou fear, or has all thy sense deserted thee? Here now we have such a gale as has not been since the memory of man; nigh two weeks has it raged, and every day it grows worse and worse. There are such waves in the firth that no man may launch a boat, and no ship live. How can any of thy foes come against thee?"

"I fear nothing save sorcery," said Grettir, "and thy life is at stake as well as mine, so do as I bid thee."

Then Noise went out and bore home a little wood, and went out for more. But the gale was so great that he

feared to go down again to the beach,
and he dreaded the labor of pulling
up the ladder that swayed so in the
wind. So he lay down by the cliff's
edge wrapped in his mantle, to watch
there. But then he fell asleep, and
slept there till evening.

That morning Thorbiorn Angle's
foster-mother said to him: "Now is it
time for thee to go to see Grettir
again."

"In such a storm!" he cried.

"That one who raised the storm
can make it less," she said. "It was
not meant for thy hurt. Get together
as many men as thou canst, for Grettir
has heard from me by this time, and
now canst thou take him, or never at
all."

So Thorbiorn, remembering what
he had seen, took some faith in her,

and went out to gather men. Ten men of his own he had, and he asked his neighbors for more, for now was the chance to do something against Grettir. They asked him how they, how many soever they might be, could win the island.

"I know not for sure," said he, "but my foster-mother has been at work, and the way is prepared."

Then one and all of them refused to help him. "Thou hast bought the island, and thou canst do thine own ridding of it. As for thy foster-mother, she is a witch, and we will not deal with her, or do anything un-Christian, for fear of the law, and of the vengeance of Grettir's kin. For if he is not won in fair and manly fashion, thou shalt regret it."

Then Thorbiorn was left to himself,

and had not men enough to go against Grettir. But he hired some with money, and tempted others with promises, till he had enough to man his larger ship, twenty men in all. They went down to the shore, and the old woman with them; the men looked at the surf, and asked how they should ever launch the ship.

"Wait a bit," said the carline, and she began to mutter spells.

So they waited a little while. Then before the boat-shed the wind began to go down, and the waves to abate, until the surf was almost gone, though everywhere else it was still high.

"Now you can go," said the crone.

But two of the men hung back, and said there was open sorcery in this, and Thorbiorn could not persuade them **to go. Thorbiorn and the others** launched the boat and put out into the waves, and behold! the wind and the sea grew less before them, so that their work was not hard. Thus they rowed out to the island, with the wind strong on either hand but a calm space round the boat; as they had started late in the afternoon, it was dusk when they came to Drangey and looked up at the ladders. And all the ladders were in place.

"So far so good," said Thorbiorn, as they drove their ship on the beach. "Now arm ye all well, and have your courage with you, for if those three defend the hut there will be work for us all."

But when they climbed the ladders, there lay Noise asleep in a sheltered place.

Angle went to him and kicked him.

"Wake!" said he. "Thou art a trusty watchman!"

Noise waked and rubbed his eyes. "Dost thou envy me my sleep?" asked he. "What more shall I do for you?"

"Fool, awake!" said Angle again. "Thy foes are before thee!"

Then Noise saw who they were, and yelled with fright; but Angle struck him in the mouth and bade him be silent, if he wished to save his life. "Now tell us," said Thorbiorn, when Noise stood quiet, "where are Grettir and Illugi?"

"They are at the hut," said Noise, "and Grettir is dying."

"How was he hurt?" asked Angle. Noise told him, and Angle laughed. "So the weak has overcome the strong," said he. "But thou, Noise, art a wretched traitor. No one will speak well of thee henceforth, though thy master was an outlaw." Then Angle tied him and left him there.

"Now," said Thorbiorn to his men, "our task is made easy for us, so follow me."

"Thou wilt not slay a bedridden man?" asked one of his men. "By the law of the land, that is murder."

"The man is an outlaw," answered Angle. "And now we must either slay these men or be slain by them, for if we stay till daylight they will find us out. And we cannot go away, for the storm is now against us."

Down at the beach the surf had changed, and was breaking fiercely on the shingle, so that no man could launch a boat there. The men saw they must put the matter through, and they said they would follow Thorbiorn.

So they went with him to the hut, and threw themselves against the door.

Within, Grettir had been dozing, and Illugi sat by his side. Now they had tamed one of the rams on the island; his head was spotted, and they called him Mottle-pate. When he was lonely, he was wont to come and butt at the door, and now Illugi thought the ram was there.

"Mottle-pate knocks hard," said he.

Grettir started from his sleep and grasped his sword. "Too hard," answered he. "Now I am glad I shall die as a man. Take thy weapons!"

Illugi snatched up his sword and shield, and just then Angle and his men threw themselves a second time against the door, and broke it down, and a man fell sprawling in. Illugi struck his head from his body.

"A mighty stroke!" said Grettir. "Thou beginnest thy man-slayings well."

Then Illugi stood within the door and guarded it, and they could do nothing against him, for he struck the heads from their spears till he had spoiled nearly all of them; and they dared not come to close quarters. Then some of them leaped up on the roof and began to tear the thatch away from above Grettir's bed. Illugi still guarded the door, but Grettir raised himself on his wounded knee, and set his sound foot on the floor, and as soon as a hole was made in the roof he thrust out his spear and slew a man, and after that another.

Then Angle saw that this would never do, for three were slain and the hut not taken. So he bade his men tear away the whole roof. They got ropes around the rafters and pulled, and pried with their spear-shafts, till they dragged the roof right off the hut. Then the men leaped over the low walls and into the hut from all sides.

Grettir now had taken his sword again, and smote on either hand of him mightily, glad of that fray. But they came at him hotly, and one leaped over the wall right upon him. Grettir struck at him as he came and clove him from the shoulder to the waist. But the body fell sprawling over him, and in the moment when Grettir was defenseless, with that weight on him, Thorbiorn thrust him in the back.

Grettir cast off the body and turned to smite Thorbiorn, but he sprang away, and Grettir fell helpless on his bed. Then Illugi fought his way to him and stood before him, and guarded him so that, though they all set on him fiercely, Grettir was not hurt again. Illugi dealt out such blows that at last they drew back before him.

"Never was such a lad as that," said Angle, "save only Grettir himself."

"How camest thou hither in this storm?" asked Grettir.

"By Christ's help," said Thorbiorn.

"Rather by the sorcery of that old woman," answered Grettir. "Neither thy strength nor thy holiness has won me."

"Still, thou art won," said Thorbiorn. Then he saw that Grettir could fight no more, and bade his men set on Illugi again. So they did, and he fought them off again, but while they battled there before the bed, Grettir sang:

"Mother, farewell!
Thou mayest tell
Thy sons were men,
By witchcraft slain.

"Not in the reek
Of chamber smoke,
Nor old and worn
I lie forlorn,

"But in battle's crash,
And mid the flash
Of sword and spear
— An outlaw's bier!"

And therewith he died.

Now when Angle saw that Grettir fought no more, and that Illugi was still giving out wounds and death, he told his men to bear him down with their shields, but first to wear him out. So they smote him with beams and spear-shafts, bruising him and wearying him; then they rushed on him with their shields held out, and though he slew still another man they took him and bound him.

Then they turned on Grettir, and tried to take the sword from him, but they could not break his grip, though all that could lay hold of his arm and hand tried there together.

"Then hew his hand off," said Thorbiorn.

So they laid the hand on a block and hewed at the wrist, and cut off the hand. Then the fingers lost their grip, and gave up the sword. Thorbiorn said the weapon was his, and took it: a great sword it was, and no man could wield it without much strength. Thorbiorn swung it with both hands, and said he would make sure of Grettir's death, and struck a great stroke upon his head. But the sword went into the skull only a little way, and a piece was broken from its edge and stayed there in the skull.

"Why wilt thou spoil the fine sword?" asked his men.

"Now all men can know it for Grettir's sword," said he. (Now that was truer than he thought, and it brought him to his death.) "And now I shall have the head, wherewith to claim the reward."

So he hewed at Grettir's neck with the sword, and struck many times, and at last cut off the head.

"Now he is truly dead," said Thorbiorn, "and till it was off I would never be sure of him."

And then he gave Illugi his choice, either to be slain there, or else to promise to do nothing against the slayers of his brother.

"I might have promised what ye ask," said Illugi, "had not this deed been done by sorcery, or had ye not slain him, bedridden as he was. But so long as I live I shall never cease to keep my feud against all who have been here."

"Then shalt thou be slain," said Thorbiorn.

Illugi laughed and said: "And death will be welcome."

Because it was murder to slay a captive man at night they kept him until morning, and then they slew him, and they buried the brothers in one cairn. When they made ready to go away they would have taken Noise with them but he went out of his head for fear of them, and wept and howled till they wearied of him, and slew him also, and buried him where he fell.

Such was the death of Grettir, a man true to his word, and undaunted in spirit, and the strongest man that ever lived in Iceland. He was forty-four years old when he was slain, and in outlawry nigh twenty years.

CHAPTER XV

THORBIORN ANGLE GETS HIS REWARD

THORBIORN ANGLE took with him Grettir's head from the island, and kept the short-sword for his own; but he divided all Grettir's goods between his men, and paid them what he promised. The gale abated suddenly, and they went ashore, and Thorbiorn boasted much of what he had done.

But his neighbors said there was nothing manly in slaying a sick man; and they said he had used sorcery, and would have nothing to do with him.

Then Thorbiorn rode in midwinter to Thorir of Garth, and claimed the

money for Grettir's death, and showed
the head.

"Put away the head out of my
sight," said Thorir. "It is true that
I hunted Grettir wherever I could,
and offered money for his death; but
witchcraft and foul murders are other
matters. If I pay the money I make
myself such a criminal as thou art, so
nothing will I pay thee."

"I will make thee, at the Althing,"
said Thorbiorn.

"We shall see what the Althing will
say of thy doings," answered Thorir.

Then Angle rode back to his house
discontented, and lived an uneasy life
until spring. Then he rode to Grettir's home at Biarg, and walked into
the hall where Asdis sat, and showed
her Grettir's head, and told her of the
slaying. Asdis looked on the head

bravely, and said: "Had he been whole when thou and thy men came to Drangey, ye would have fled before him even as Haering fled before Illugi. But what dost thou here?"

"I come to seize Illugi's goods," said Thorbiorn, "for he was made outlaw by defending his brother."

"Stay a little while," said Asdis, "and thou mayest have all thou canst take."

But then Angle's men called out to him that men were coming riding over the hills, and so he hastily went away. Those men were Grettir's kinsmen, and the younger wished to ride after him to slay him, but the older men restrained them, till such time as the Althing had pronounced on the whole matter.

When it came time for men to ride

to the Althing, Thorbiorn made ready to go to press his suit for the head-money, and to sue for Illugi's goods. His brother said to him: "Wilt thou take Grettir's head with thee?"

"Yes, of course," said he.

"His kinsmen will slay thee at the first sight of it," said his brother. "Better bury it here."

Thorbiorn said he would not do that, and took it with him a little way on his journey. But then he thought better, and buried it in a hillock which has since been called Grettir's hillock. He went to the Althing, and brought up his causes, and pressed them hard.

But Thorir of Garth said he would pay no money for Grettir until he was compelled. And then Grettir's kin brought an action of outlawry against

Thorbiorn, for his sorcery, and for slaying a sick man.

And then before the courts, by all the judges, Angle was banished from Iceland, and he was to stay away so long as there lived in the land any of Grettir's kin who were alive at the time of Grettir's slaying. All Thorbiorn's men were outlawed with him, and none of those who fell were to be atoned, and all suits against Grettir fell to the ground.

Then Thorbiorn secretly fled away from the Althing, lest he be slain there and then, so great was the hatred of him. He got a few of his goods from his home, and lived for a while in hiding, till he could take ship to Norway. Grettir's kin were hot after him, to slay him, but at last he went away from the land, and got to Norway, and thought himself safe. There he gave out that he had slain Grettir, and told only so much of the story as he chose. But one day a man said to him:

"Some have told another story than thou tellest. And again we marvel that thou sayest anything at all of that slaying, since Grettir has a brother dwelling here in the land, who is a man of riches and power."

Then Angle's jaw fell, and he began again to fear, and thought what he should do. At last he fled out of Norway, and crossed all Europe, and came to Constantinople. There he took service with the Emperor, in his Varangian guard. The men were all Norsemen, but Angle gave himself another name, and for a long time thought himself safe.

Now word had been brought to Thorstein Dromund, Grettir's brother, of Grettir's slaying, and how the slayer had come to Norway. Thorstein called to mind what he had said in years gone by, how his thin arms should avenge Grettir. Then he went about seeking Angle, and at last he learned that he had taken ship from the land.

So Thorstein sent word out to Iceland: "Send me the piece that was broken from Grettir's sword." Grettir's kin had just then sent for those two bodies from Drangey, and for Grettir's head, to give them Christian burial. They picked from the skull the piece of the sword, and sent it to Dromund. He put it in his purse and followed on the track of Thorbiorn Angle, and went after him from place to place till he came to Constantinople. And there Dromund likewise took service with the Varangians.

Yet for all that he was no nearer to discovering Grettir's slayer, for Angle hid his name, and the two had never met. But one day it happened that the guard was to be sent out against a foe, and they were called together for a weapon-show, for it was the custom in those days that before the guard went out to battle all men should show their weapons for their leaders to see.

It came to Angle's turn, and he showed his weapons, and among them the short-sword. Because of the beauty of the sword it was much admired, but the nick in the blade was deemed a defect, and they asked him how it had been made.

Then Thorbiorn, thinking himself safe, boasted foolishly. Said he: "This was the sword of Grettir the Strong, of whom many skalds sing. He was so

strong that no man could match him
until I met him. But I slew him, and
hewed off his head with his own sword
(now to slay a man with his own
weapon was a disgrace to him), and in
so doing this nick was made in the
blade."

That was a great marvel to them,
for all had heard of Grettir, but the
news of his death had not yet come to
that far-away place. So they handed
the short-sword about, and praised it
much.

Then Thorstein Dromund reached
out his hand and took the sword, and
drew out from his purse the piece of
steel that had been taken from Grettir's
head. He set the piece into the blade,
and it fitted perfectly. Then he said:
"Yea, this was Grettir's sword, for
this is the piece that was broken out

of it. And I am Grettir's brother, that have come here for my vengeance. Thus I fulfil it."

Then he swung high the sword, with both his hands, and ran upon Angle. He stood still in astonishment, and made no move to defend himself. The sword fell upon his head, and clove it to the very jaw, and down he fell, slain by his own weapon.

Thus was Grettir avenged, and no Icelander before or since has been avenged so far from his home.

Thorstein Dromund got himself home after many dangers, and lived in Norway till he was an old man. Then he went to Rome, where he died a monk.

And thus ends the story of Grettir the Strong. His doings, his songs, and his sayings, with the tale of the vengeance for him, were treasured in the minds of men, and told at firesides, till after many years they were gathered and written down, and have been printed and spread abroad in many tongues, until here they are told again, eight centuries and three-quarters after Grettir's death.